C000068243

Derbyshire
Churches and Chapels
Open to Visitors

compiled by
Rodney Tomkins
member of the Derby Diocesan Advisory
Committee for the Care of Churches

illustrated by
Elisabeth Stoppard

with a Foreword by

The Right Reverend Jonathan S Bailey
Bishop of Derby

Scarthin Books
Cromford
2000

First Printing 2000
Scarthin Books, Cromford, Derbyshire, England
http://www.scarthinbooks.demon.co.uk
email: claire@scarthinbooks.demon.co.uk

Text © 2000 Rodney Tomkins

Design and Illustrations by Elisabeth Stoppard
Typesetting by Michael Susko
lis.and.mike@susko.demon.co.uk

Printed by Bell & Bain Ltd., Glasgow

ISBN 1900446022

Foreword

by
The Right Reverend Jonathan S Bailey
Bishop of Derby

The Churches and Chapels of Derbyshire have been described in many ways before by virtue of architectural and historical merit. Indeed we have world-leading treasures on our doorstep here. But these ancient and modern stones are used and loved by "living stones", the Christian people of our own generation. This new book points to their worship and other activities as well as the building and its contents. I warmly commend this resource to its readers, and pray God's blessing for all who will visit the places and communities it describes.

Acknowledgements

To have compiled a work of reference such as this would have been impossible without much assistance from helpers on the ground. In particular I must mention the contribution by The Revd Clive Thrower, Derby Diocesan Tourism Officer, who has enthusiastically backed the project and brought into operation his various communications facilities, and likewise The Revd John Bland, Information Officer for the Nottingham & Derby District of the Methodist Church. Other denominational officers who have also willingly distributed questionnaires on my behalf include Mr John Butlin (Baptist Union), Mr Don Hamilton (Congregational Federation), The Revd Anne Brown and The Revd Paul Wilson (Methodist, Sheffield and Manchester Districts respectively), Ms Valerie Bearn (Society of Friends) and The Revd Paul Breeze (United Reformed). To all of these I must express my gratitude for their interest and support. Then, of course, I must thank the countless individual clergy and church officers who have responded to the questionnaires and who have supplied me with a wealth of interesting information regarding their places of worship. I can only hope that they feel it to have been a worthwhile exercise that will ultimately bring benefit to their causes. To the Revd John Drackley (former Secretary of the Derby Diocesan Advisory Committee) I am greatly indebted for his interest and encouragement in checking through the script and filling in some gaps in the information.

Finally I must thank The Right Revd Jonathan Bailey, Bishop of Derby, for his great kindness in consenting to write the Foreword to this handbook.

Rodney Tomkins
Duffield
September 1999

Preface

The inspiration for the format of this handbook has been a similar work of reference published annually by the Scotland's Churches Scheme. It is hoped that, far from being just another guide-book, it will go some way towards encouraging tourists and others to visit a particular church or chapel and thereby experience something of the actual living, worshipping, out-going community in that place - something that may be achieved by such means as well-presented displays, photographs of parish personalities and events, up-to-date notice boards, bookstalls, children's information, welcoming guides, pastoral assistance, as well as just the opportunity for some peace and quiet. Some churches understandably do not feel able to leave the building open and unattended as a normal rule, though are prepared to have somebody on duty for a limited period - even just an hour or so a week (preferably with some lights on) is worth doing. In other instances the regular coffee morning or annual flower festival may be an ideal opportunity to open up. Failing any of these an approved contact number or address will suffice to be included under our general umbrella of "willingness to open".

Some churches have unfortunately failed to respond in time for publication. Non-inclusion does not necessarily indicate therefore that a church is not open to the public on any weekdays. All information has been supplied with the good-will and co-operation of the individual ministers and officers; it is reproduced here in good faith as being accurate at the time of writing. Circumstances change, however, and it is inevitable that some information may become obsolete: we can only apologise for the occasional disappointment that may arise and hope that we will get it right next time. It is fully our intention to up-date the handbook at reasonable intervals and requests for inclusion or amendment will be welcomed by the author or publisher.

Background to the Churches and Chapels of Derbyshire

Of nearly 400 Anglican parish churches and chapels-of-ease at present in the county, barely a third of that number display recognizable mediaeval origins. And of these a number of present-day parochial churches were originally built as chapelries within the one-time very large parishes (such as Duffield and Tideswell, to quote just two) that were a feature of the exceptionally extensive mediaeval diocese of Lichfield. Following a period under Southwell the modern diocese of Derby, comprising virtually the whole county, was created in 1927.

The only mediaeval building now used by the Roman Catholics is the Padley Chapel at Grindleford - a site of poignant memories in Catholic recusant history. Two further "chapels" pre-dating the Catholic "Emancipation" of 1829 are at Hassop and Hathersage. The southern half of the county now forms part of the diocese of Nottingham while the north comes within that of Hallam (Sheffield)

Congregationalists, Unitarians and English Presbyterians are all derived from a common source - the independent puritan congregations of the 17th century. There was some confusion by the earlier 18th century as to which branch of development these groups would follow, but by the end of the century they had sorted themselves into clear (though not necessarily organized) denominations. The majority of Congregationalists and Presbyterians combined in 1972 to form the United Reformed Church, though a substantial minority of the former body still chose to continue an independent tradition within the continuing Congregational Federation.

Baptists were also to be found among the early independent congregations, but very soon their beliefs regarding adult baptism led them into their own movement. Many early Baptists were of the "strict" (Calvinist) type but, by the 19th century, it was the "open" (General) Baptists who were to predominate in Derbyshire. The present-day Baptist Union dates from 1891.

The Quakers (Society of Friends) are yet another group whose dissenting origins lie in the 17th century. With no formal creeds or worship patterns, however, they seem not to have been prone to the sort of internal controversy that has led other bodies into bitter disintegration in the course of their histories. On the other hand their sometimes misunderstood policy of peaceful resistance laid them open, during the earlier decades, to persecution from all quarters.

The Methodist movement started in the mid-18th century as a break-away from Anglicanism (though not initially by any choice of its founder, John

Wesley). The Primitive Methodists split from the Wesleyans in the early 1800's and soon became particularly strong in Derbyshire (where they were first referred to as "Ranters"); a number of other secessionist reforming groups appeared soon afterwards. Some re-alignments took place in the middle of the century, leaving four main Methodist bodies - Wesleyans (the mainstream group), Primitives (the second largest), United Methodist Free Church and the Wesleyan Reform Union. These eventually re-united, for the most part, in 1932 to form the present Methodist Church, but a number of small Reform Chapels - especially in the Dales villages - still remain outside this union.

The simple early buildings of the dissenters were referred to as "Meeting Houses". It was John Wesley who preferred the word "Chapel", with its correct ecclesiastical implication of being a place of worship subordinate to the main church of the parish. The term was adopted generally by non-conformists from the early 1800's until, eventually, the use of the word "Church" came to be regarded as adding a bit more "class" to the increasingly grandiose structures that were appearing later in that century.

European Heritage Weekend

This is observed annually on the second weekend of September.

At the time of writing details are not to hand of what will be available in September 2000, or beyond. However, if 1999 is anything to go by, there should be on view to the public an interesting assortment of historic buildings of all types - many of them not normally open on a regular basis.

To coincide with this event the Derbyshire Churches & Chapels Preservation Trust (together with similar bodies in many other counties) organize a sponsored bike ride (or hike) around as many places of worship as the participants can reach. This event always takes place on the Saturday of Heritage Weekend, with a large number of such places being open all day to welcome those who are taking part. Sponsored proceeds are shared between the DCCPT and the church or chapel of the participants choice.

Heritage Weekend is clearly therefore a highly recommendable occasion for a "church crawl".

The use of the Handbook

The county has been divided up into fifteen clearly defined areas, each around a central town or large village. These areas correspond roughly to the useful pattern already established by the Anglican deaneries. Within each area the entries are arranged in a purely alphabetical manner regardless of denomination.

Symbols Used

P Convenient parking

D Bookstall with guide-books, souvenirs, etc.

▣ Exhibition

♟ Children-orientated information

♟ Welcomers or guides on duty

☕ Refreshments available

♿ Convenient access for disabled people

WC Toilets on premises

1st, 2nd 3rd are shorthands for 1st, 2nd, 3rd Sunday in the month.

Most churches and many chapels are now "listed" as being of architectural interest and are therefore subject to more stringent planning regulations. The older system (still in use in many urban areas) was to award religious buildings with Grades A, B or C; the newer, general system is to give Grades I, II* or II. To avoid invidious comparisons of grading only the prestigious "A" or "I" grades are indicated in the text.

At the back are some suggested "trails" which may help the intending visitor to develop certain special interest themes.

Contents

Alfreton

ALFRETON St Martin, Church Street

SK 407 559

A large church in a well-kept, garden-like churchyard, away from the bustle of the town's main streets. Its origins go back to c1170 when it was in the gift of Beauchief Abbey (Sheffield). Nave, lean-to south aisle and tower are still mostly of C14 and C15. The very wide north aisle, however, was rebuilt in 1868 and is larger than the nave; the chancel was lengthened by 10 feet during 1899-1901. The chancel screen was erected in 1921 and the rood figures came from St Andrew's in Derby (demolished in 1968). The large organ, originally by the French builder, August Gern, was acquired from Dover College in 1952; it was totally rebuilt and redesigned by Henry Groves & Son in 1999.

SUNDAY SERVICES: 8.00, 9.30 (10.00 on 3rd), 6.00 (1st & 3rd only)
CONTACT: (01773) 833280 (Vicar) or (01773) 834002 (Mr Marson)
P (Leisure Centre) &

BLACKWELL St Werburgh, Church Hill

SK 444 583

As its address suggests, the church enjoys a position on high ground, looking over an area that has been (though is no longer) associated with coal mining since mediaeval times. Of the original late C12 church there remains but one pillar, in Transitional style, preserved on the inner face of the north wall. The tower dates from an 1828 rebuild while the rest of the church is of 1878. In the porch is the stump of a Saxon cross.

SUNDAY SERVICES: 9.30, 6.00 (4.00 in winter)
CONTACT: (01773) 836885 (Mr Corbishley)
OPEN FOR FLOWER FESTIVAL (June) & HARVEST (October)
P (street) & WC

1

CRICH St Mary, Cromford Road (Grade I)

SK 348 546

The village straggles up the side of an eminence which eventually rises to a height of nearly 1,000 feet. The church is at the top end of the village and is of substantial Norman origin, though it is the C14 tower and spire that form its most prominently visible feature. Once inside one notices the squat Norman arches of the north arcade with their chubby pillars and also the low sill level of the large and very elegant C14 east window. In an elevated position at the west end of the nave is the 1914 Hill organ, an important relic of the final year of that famous firm but now, sadly, silent.

SUNDAY SERVICES: 8.00, 10.00, 6.30
CHURCH OPEN: daily 9.00-4.00
CONTACT: Mrs Hooton, 22 Cromford Road or (01773) 852449 (Vicar)
Publication: "A Brief Tour Around St Mary's Church, Crich"
Ⓟ (street) 🚪 ♿ wc

IRONVILLE Christ Church, Casson Street

SK 446 519

The model village and its associated canal basin were built by the Butterley Iron Company, 1834-1860, as a failed project to create an inland harbour (killed, of course, by the early advent of railways). The church itself was built in 1852 and is interesting, not only for its cruciform plan but also for its considerable constructional use of iron. The organ, of outstanding tonal quality, was built in 1876 by T C Lewis for a private house in London.

SUNDAY SERVICE: 11.00
CONTACT: (01773) 602241 (Vicar)
Ⓟ (church hall) ☕ (Thurs 10.00-11.00 in church hall)

MORTON Holy Cross

SK 406 601

The church and its setting continue to preserve a village atmosphere. Of the mediaeval building the C13 north arcade and C15 tower still remain; there is also a Saxon font, C15 screen, C17 pulpit and communion table, and an 1864 organ by Brindley. In the churchyard a yew tree was planted to commemorate the coronation of King George V.

SUNDAY SERVICES: rota as advertised
CONTACT: (01773) 836003 (Incumbent) or (01773) 872332 (Mr Higgon)
 or (01773) 872354 Mrs Taylor
P (street & Rectory Room) 🗋 ⚑ ♿ wc

PENTRICH St Matthew, Main Road (Grade I)

SK 389 526

The village is well known for its associations with the so-called Pentrich Revolution of 1817. The earliest parts of the church itself are the lower tower and the nave arcades, all of late C12, while the profuse battlements on nave, aisles, porch and tower represent a major rebuilding in the Perpendicular period.

SUNDAY SERVICES: 9.30 (weekly), 6.30 (1st & 2nd)
CHURCH OPEN: Sat 2.00-4.00
CONTACT: (01773) 607307 or (01773) 746756 (Churchwardens)
P (street & village hall) ♦ wc

RIDDINGS St James, Church Street

SK 429 528

The church, by Francis Bedford (1832), is attractively set amidst an important conservation area comprising the estate village built by local ironworks master, James Oakes. It should ideally be seen as part of a general visit and, to this end, Amber Valley Borough Council have published a useful guide leaflet, "A Walk Around Riddings". The chancel was extended in 1884 and the fine, wrought iron screen is by P H Currey (1906). The large 3-manual organ, recently rebuilt, has pipework going back to an early C19 instrument by Bevington.

SUNDAY SERVICE: 9.00 (9.45 on 2nd)
CONTACT: (01773) 602241 (Incumbent)
P (street) ♿ wc

SOMERCOTES St Thomas, Nottingham Road

SK 429 539

Chancel, side chapel and vestry were consecrated in 1854. The remainder was completed by P H Currey in 1902; the carved reredos dates from 1910. Following a bad fire in 1980 the church was reconstructed by Montague Associates of Derby. As so often happens, the trauma of a fire (or other catastrophe) provides an opportunity for general enhancement. Here at St Thomas we have a refurbished interior that is attractive (in the Anglo-Catholic tradition), comfortable and well-appointed. The present organ, replacing one that was destroyed in the fire, is a fine 1884 instrument by Binns. The churchyard is being planted with indigenous hedges and shrubs to encourage wildlife and create a peaceful area within the urban environment.

SUNDAY SERVICES: 9.30, 6.00
CHURCH OPEN: Fri 9.00-12.00 & for coffee on 1st Sat 10.00-11.30
CONTACT: (01773) 602840 (Mr Brooksbank) or (01773) 541994 (Mr Stone)
P ⓖ WC

SOUTH NORMANTON St Michael, Church Street

SK 442 570

The church displays architectural features from C13 to C19, most important perhaps being the 15th century tower. The organ is a fine 1890's instrument by Kirkland of which the eight largest wooden pedal pipes are placed, somewhat incongruously, against the south wall of the chancel, there being no room for them in the chamber.

SUNDAY SERVICES: 10.30, 6.30
CONTACT: (01773) 811273 (Rector)
P (street)

SOUTH WINGFIELD All Saints, Holme Lane

SK 383 558

The church is attractively situated, well back from the B5035 road and close by the River Amber. Though the main structure is C13 the nave and aisle windows were refurbished in 1803 in a plain Classical style. Adjacent to the chancel exterior wall is an interesting C13 cross-legged effigy of a knight. The church also possesses "The Strelley Bible" (1712) - a bound volume containing Book of Common Prayer (1712), a "Breeches" Bible (c1576) and a Psalter (1583)

SUNDAY SERVICE: 11.00 (10.00 on 1st)
CONTACT: (01773) 833667 (Mrs Marshall) or (01773) 833550 (Mr Szabo)
Publications: guide leaflet & "The Strelley Bible"
P (street)

STONEBROOM St Peter, High Street

SK 416 597

Small church in Arts and Crafts style by P H Currey (consecrated 1907).

SUNDAY SERVICES: rota as advertised
CONTACT: (01773) 874552 (Mrs Joyce)
P (at rear) ♿ wc

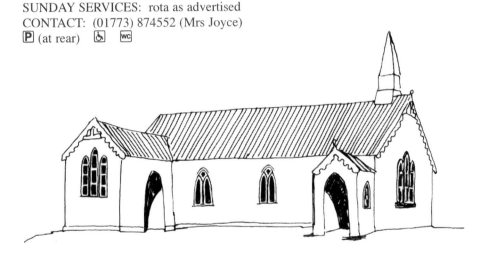

St Saviour, Swanwick

SWANWICK Baptist, Derby Road

SK 404 535

The chapel was first built soon after the foundation of the church in 1794. Originally a wide structure, in the manner of the early meeting houses, it was extended forwards (towards the main road) in 1828, resulting in a square plan. At the same time the rear gallery was erected in the new extension; the pulpit is also of this date. There is a schoolroom at the back and an old graveyard on both the Derby Road and Chapel Street sides.

SUNDAY SERVICES: 10.45, 6.00
CHURCH OPEN: Tue, 9.00-1.00 ("In Touch" - drop-in centre)
CONTACT: (01773) 606043 (Minister)
P (street) wc

SWANWICK St Andrew, Derby Road

SK 404 532

The church occupies a prominent site at the main crossroads in the centre of the village. Consecrated in 1860, it is to a design by Benjamin Wilson of Derby; the tower dates from 1902. A triptych was painted by a WWII German prisoner at nearby "The Hayes" (now an important inter-denominational conference centre). The organ is a large, well preserved 2-manual by Nicholson & Lord (1885).

SUNDAY SERVICES: 8.00 (1st & 3rd), 11.00, 6.30 (2nd & 4th)
CHURCH OPEN: Tue & Fri 2.00-4.00
CHURCH OFFICE: Old School House (opposite) (01773) 541458
P (public CP on B6016 towards Pentrich) 🏛 🚹 ♿ wc

SWANWICK St Saviour, Midland Railway Centre

SK 415 517

This typical "tin tabernacle" formerly stood in Westhouses (Parish of Blackwell) where it was consecrated in 1898. During the 1990's it became redundant and was acquired by the Midland Railway Trust for their museum site at Swanwick. It has been restored and appropriately furnished, and occasionally houses exhibitions.

CHURCH OPEN: during railway opening hours

ASHBOURNE

ALSOP-EN-LE-DALE St Michael & All Angels

SK 160 551

A Norman church in a picturesque rural setting. The most interesting feature is perhaps the south door with its unusual double chevron ornament.There are scratch dials to be found on the south wall.

SUNDAY SERVICE: 11.00 (no service on 1st)
CHURCH OPEN: daily, 10.00 till dusk
[P] (street)

ASHBOURNE Methodist, Church Street

SK 179 465

Built 1880 and extended 1900; of brick with stone dressings. The front elevation, with Corinthian columns, pediment and twin towers, looks toward the Edwardian style of Baroque, and this is further emphasized by the quasi-theatrical "proscenium" arch opening into the choir/organ area. The entire premises have recently been refurbished to a high standard. In the basement (former day school) is residential accommodation for youth weekends, conferences, etc., while the old lock-up shops on the street corner are now the "Cornerstone" coffee shop (open Thur to Sat 10.00-3.30)

SUNDAY SERVICES: 10.30, 6.30
CONTACT: (01335) 342810
[P] (adjacent)   [☕] (coffee shop)   [wc] (coffee shop)

ASHBOURNE St John, Buxton Road
SK 180 470

A large church of 1871 in what the Germans call "Rundbogenstil" (literally "round arch style" - a free adaptation of Romanesque). The result is a spacious, open interior with slender arcades and excellent acoustical properties.

SUNDAY SERVICES: 9.15 (weekly), 3.00 (2nd & 4th only)
CONTACT: (01335) 346058 (Mrs Wareing)
[P] (at rear)   [wc]

ASHBOURNE St Oswald, Church Street (Grade A)

SK 176 464

One of the great churches of Derbyshire, cruciform in plan, with a slender spire 212 feet in height. To pick out only a few important features: the long Early English chancel with its large Perpendicular east window containing glass by Kempe, the curiously lop-sided lack of a north nave aisle, the large chapels forming the eastern half of both transepts - the northern one containing mediaeval tombs of the Cockaynes; there are fragments of C13 glass in the north transept and also within Kempe's east window. Visitors are recommended to come in Spring when the churchyard is full of daffodils.

SUNDAY SERVICES: 8.00, 10.30, 6.30
CHURCH OPEN: daily, from 8.30
Publications: numerous
P (street)   📖

ATLOW SS Philip & James

SK 231 486

A small, simple but attractive church on a rural hillside, built in 1874. It is of stone construction though the interior is enlivened, in a somewhat Italian manner, with red bricks and glazed tiles.

SUNDAY SERVICE: 10.45 (2nd), 6.30 (4th)
CONTACT: (01335) 370546 (Mrs Kniveton)
P (street or village hall)

BRADLEY All Saints

SK 224 459

An aisleless nave and chancel, all of C14, and without any tower. The altar rails are of local workmanship, late C17 or C18. In the churchyard is a stone cross beheaded by Cromwell's soldiers

SUNDAY SERVICE: 9.00 (1st), 10.45 (2nd & 4th), 6.30 (3rd)
CHURCH OPEN: daily, 9.00-5.00 (summer)
CONTACT: (01335) 370578 (Mr Mitchell)
P (opposite)

CLIFTON Holy Trinity

SK 165 448

Built in 1845 (architect: H I Stevens, of Derby) with later tower and apse - the latter features providing an attractively decorative element. As for the interior, the lofty chancel arch gives an impressive feeling of spaciousness. The 2-manual Conacher organ dates from 1907.

SUNDAY SERVICE: 9.30
CONTACT: (01335) 343233 (Mr Watkins)
  (ramp available)

FENNY BENTLEY St Edmund, Ashes Lane

SK 175 502

Norman nave and c1300 chancel with Victorian north aisle, tower and spire sums up the architecture. It is perhaps the furnishings that are of most interest, particularly the fine C16 screen. The NE chapel contains tombs of the Beresford family who lived at the nearby C15 fortified Old Hall; it has a ceiling with panels painted on aluminium (1895, the first known commercial use of this material). Within the chancel the east window was designed by Norman Shaw (1877) and the altar, cross and candlesticks are by Advent Hunstone (of Tideswell, 1939).

SUNDAY SERVICE: 6.30 (3.30 in winter)
CHURCH OPEN: daily (summer)
CONTACT: (01335) 350537 (Mr Smith) P (street)

St Edmund, Fenny Bentley

HOGNASTON St Bartholomew

SK 236 506

The oldest part of the church is the Norman south wall and the interesting C12 tympanum over the south door. The latter is quite fantastic and contains what is assumed to be an "Agnus Dei" representation, together with a bishop and various animal figures - including the Hognaston "Hog". Externally the massive though squat tower is supported by a single large buttress in the middle of its west side. The village enjoys a peaceful calm since the construction of nearby Carsington Reservoir and its new bypass road.

SUNDAY SERVICE: 9.00 (1st), 10.45 (2nd, 3rd & 4th)
CHURCH OPEN: daily, 9.00-5.00 (summer)
FLOWER FESTIVAL: for 5 days from Ascension
CONTACT: (01335) 370554 (Mr Dawson)
P (street) wc

HULLAND Christ Church

SK 249 474

A neat little church dating from 1838, whose simplicity and compactness likens it almost to a model kit. The simple, aisleless nave still retains its two-decker pulpit, box pews and west gallery; the original shallow sanctuary, however, was extended in 1961 to form a small chancel. The setting, at the top end of the village, is delightfully rural and the large churchyard gives good views over open, rolling countryside.

SUNDAY SERVICE: 10.00 (1st), 9.15 (2nd, 3rd & 4th)
CHURCH OPEN: daily, 9.00-5.00 (summer)
CONTACT: (01335) 370403 (Mrs Johns)
Publication: "Christ Church Hulland 1838-1988 A Country Church and its Parish"
P (in road) 🕯 wc

KNIVETON St Michael & All Angels (Grade I)

SK 210 503

The church snuggles on a hillside site overlooking the small village in the valley below. The aisleless nave is Norman, its south doorway having a bear carved on the keystone - any connection with the contemporary animal carvings at nearby Hognaston (above)? The small tower and spire are of C13 while the low chancel dates from the C15. Fragments of C14 and C15 glass, conserved by the York Glaziers' Trust, are to be found in the south sanctuary window.

SUNDAY SERVICE: 11.00 (1st & 3rd only)
CHURCH OPEN: daily, 9.00-5.00 (summer)
CONTACT: (01335) 342243 (Mrs Hopkin)
[P] (street)

St Mary, Mappleton

MAPPLETON St Mary

SK 165 480

The delightfully whimsical little building is on a slope overlooking the River Dove and the grounds of Okeover Hall. It dates from the C18 and is of simple, unsophisticated design and craftsmanship - quite simply a nave and small chancel, both with round topped windows, and a squat tower bearing an octagonal dome surmounted by a domed lantern. The interior is plain and simple, apart from a very prettily encased small modern organ by Wood of Huddersfield.

SUNDAY SERVICE: 9.15
CHURCH OPEN: at same time as Post Office (otherwise key available from there)
[P] (street)

NORBURY St Mary & St Barlok (Grade I)

SK 126 424

An outstanding building by any reckoning. The fairly small, aisled nave, mostly of the C15, has the tower over the middle bay of its south aisle, thus giving the nave an unusually symmetrical side facade when viewed from the churchyard. East of this, and marginally longer though without aisles, is the magnificently lofty C14 chancel with four large windows each side, all containing mostly c1340 glass; together with the great east window this chancel has indeed been described as "a lantern in stone". Within the chancel lie the C15 tombs of the Fitzherbert family. George Eliot (of "Adam Bede" fame) was born in the parish and sang in the church choir.

SUNDAY SERVICE: 11.00
CHURCH OPEN: daily
CONTACT: (01335) 324225 (Mr Clowes)
Publication: "Church of St Mary & St Barlock Norbury"
Ⓟ (in drive to Norbury Hall)   ⛪

St Mary & St Barlok, Norbury

PARWICH St Peter

SK 188 544

The setting is a small and unspoilt limestone village - one that is remote from any of the main through roads. Around the village pond is a jumble of little lanes and greens. The church itself is in neo-Norman style, 1874, though relics of genuine Norman, including the original chancel arch, are now to be seen reset in the tower. The attractively painted organ case by Walter Tapper was added to the c1874 Abbott instrument in 1907.

St. Peter, Snelston

SUNDAY SERVICE: 9.30 (2nd & 3rd), 10.00 (4th), 6.30 (1st)
CHURCH OPEN: daily
P (street) 🕯

SNELSTON St Peter

SK 155 433

Only the tower is old, the remainder having been twice rebuilt - in 1825 and again in 1907. It is this later rebuild that gives the church its character - the best feature being the west gable, as seen across the fields, with its French Gothic doorway surmounted by statue and rose window. The church is an important element within the ensemble of a very pretty, early C19 estate village.

SUNDAY SERVICE: 9.30
CONTACT: (01335) 324208 (Mrs Upton)
P (street)

St Mary, Tissington

THORPE St Leonard (Grade I)

SK 157 502

The church enjoys a privileged setting within a picturesque village surrounded by the hills of Dovedale. It is small, with a low but massive Norman tower, a Norman nave and a rebuilt (and extended) chancel. Furnishings include an Elizabethan communion rail and an interesting chamber organ by Bishop (c1840). In the churchyard is a sundial of 1767.

SUNDAY SERVICES: 9.30 (1st), 11.00 (2nd & 3rd), 11.15 (4th), 6.30 (2nd : summer only)
CHURCH OPEN: daily, 9.00 till dusk
Publication: D H Buckley, "The Parish of Thorpe and The Church of St Leonard"
P (street) ⊡ ⚲ ⚲ ⊡ ♿ wc

TISSINGTON Methodist, Chapel Lane
SK 178 525

A simple building, dating from 1955, of coursed limestone with gritstone dressings - appropriate materials for its location within an ancient and historic village much visited by tourists.

SUNDAY SERVICE: 2.30 (2nd only)
CHAPEL OPEN: daily
P (in front)

[Linked with Tissington, though just in Staffordshire, is MILLDALE Methodist,
SK 139 548.

This small chapel, built in 1835, is also open daily, though without regular Sunday services.
P - public CP 1/2-mile]

TISSINGTON St Mary
SK 176 532

This village is familiar to the many thousands who throng there in the summer months, especially at the time of the celebrated Well Dressings. It is said that no building has taken place in the village since 1900 - neither is there an inn or public house. The church is on a mound, across the green from the sprawling Hall, home of the FitzHerbert family since the C17. It is a Norman church, rather bizarrely re-Normanized in 1854 when the north aisle was added. Still genuinely Norman is the chancel arch, though partly covered over (who would allow this nowadays?) by an enormous C17 monument; further FitzHerbert memorials are to be found within the chancel. Communion rail and two-decker pulpit are both from c1600 while two mid-C19 windows in the chancel south wall contain roundels depicting The Flood and Noah's Ark.

SUNDAY SERVICE: 8.00 (3rd), 11.00 (1st), 6.30 (2nd & 4th)
CHURCH OPEN: daily, 9.00 till dusk
P (street - public CP at peak periods)

BAKEWELL & EYAM

ASHFORD-IN-THE-WATER Holy Trinity

SK 194 697

The mediaeval church was almost completely rebuilt in 1868-70. Surviving features include the C13 tower and a Norman tympanum over the south door depicting a Tree of Life flanked by a lion and a pig; there is also a Jacobean pulpit and stained glass by William Morris and Burne-Jones. Hanging from the ceiling are four Virgin Crowns (funeral garlands of young maidens), the oldest dating from 1747.

SUNDAY SERVICE: 9.45
CHURCH OPEN: daily, 9.00 till dusk
WELL DRESSING & PATRONAL
FESTIVAL: all week from Trinity
Sunday
P (street & Court Lane) ⬠

BAKEWELL All Saints
(Grade A)

SK 215 685

The very large, cruciform church enjoys a commanding position above the small market town. The Norman west front still survives though much of the remainder, including the unusual octagonal central tower and spire, was rebuilt or very much restored during the C19. Other

The Foljambe monument,
All Saints Bakewell

architectural features of interest include the twin east windows at the end of the long chancel and the enormous south transept - almost as long as the nave - containing tombs of the Vernon family from nearby Haddon Hall.

SUNDAY SERVICES: 8.00, 10.45, 6.30
CHURCH OPEN: daily, 8.30-5.30
Publications: various
P (public CP 200 yds - but not always easy!) ⬠ ♿

BAKEWELL English Martyrs (RC), Buxton Road

SK 217 687

A chapel-of-ease in lancet Gothic style, built in 1890 and served from Hassop (see below).

SUNDAY MASS: 10.30 (1st), 9.00 (other Suns)
CHURCH OPEN: mornings, 9.15-10.00
Ⓟ (public CP) ♿

BAKEWELL Friends' Meeting House, Chapel Row, Matlock Street

SK 218 683

The Meeting House was built in stone in 1852 and is next to the burial ground. Here the gravestones are laid flat in the grass and are all of the same style - as witness to the Friends' beliefs regarding simplicity and equality. The interior has been modernized to suit present usage, but the original Elders' bench remains.

SUNDAY WORSHIP:
10.30
CONTACT: (01629)
812712 (Bookings Clerk)
Ⓟ (limited amount in
courtyard) wc

Doorway of
All Saints, Bakewell

BAKEWELL Methodist

SK 217 684

The Victorian Gothic former Wesleyan chapel was completely refurbished in 1992 with all modern facilities. The church itself is accessible most days since most of the rooms are in use for some purpose or other.

SUNDAY SERVICES: 10.45, 6.30
CHURCH OPEN: most days (see above)
OPEN FOR COFFEE: Mon 10.00-12.00 (lunches on BH)
CHURCH OFFICE: Thurs & Fri 9.00-11.00 (01629) 812135
P 🕯 ♿ wc

BEELEY St Anne, Church Lane

SK 265 677

The church is at the north end of one of Chatsworth's attractive estate villages. Its Norman south door and C14 tower survived a major rebuild and then a "restoration", both in the C19.

SUNDAY SERVICES (all BCP): 9.30 (weekly), 6.00 (2nd & 4th, Easter to Harvest, then 2.30)
CONTACT: (01629) 732651 (Mrs Grafton)
P (street)

BRADWELL St Barnabas

SK 175 811

Bradwell prospered from lead mining during the C18 and C19; it also became a centre for milliners and hatters. The building of the church and vicarage in the 1860's was partly funded by Samuel Fox, inventor of the folding umbrella. Pulpit and altar rails have C18 carved panels said to have come "from a college chapel". The historic 1869 Brindley organ (recently restored) was the gift of Sir W Jackson, MP for North Derbyshire. In the churchyard is the grave of a pedlar who paid for the bells. Clearly Bradwell Church would have been much the poorer without the generosity of its C19 parishioners!

SUNDAY SERVICES: 9.15 (8.00 + 10.00 on 2nd)
CHURCH OPEN: daily, 9.00 till dusk
OPEN FOR GALA WEEK EXHIBITION: 1st week August
P (street, or school yard during holidays) ♿ wc

CASTLETON St Edmund

SK 150 829

The setting of the village is magnificent, with Lose Hill to the north and lying in the shadow of Peveril Castle on its high rock to the south. The exterior impression of the nave is that of the early C19 rebuilding. Once inside, however, there is still much that is venerable - the fine Norman chancel arch, the early C17 ceiling and the late C17 box pews. Most fascinating of all is the late Georgian library (visible through a locked glass door), left by a former Incumbent "to be lent out to the parishioners at the discretion of the minister". The church also possesses copies of "Vinegar" and "Breeches" Bibles.

SUNDAY SERVICES: 8.00, 11.00
CHURCH OPEN: daily, 9.00 till dusk
GARLAND CEREMONY: last Sat May
CHURCH FESTIVAL: last week August
P (street or public CP) 🚻 ♿

CHATSWORTH HOUSE Private Chapel

SK 260 703

Completed in 1694, this is an exuberant Baroque interior in the real Continental sense of the word. It is dominated by the two-storey, pedimented alabaster reredos with its painting of Doubting Thomas by Verrio. Above is the magnificent painted ceiling by Thornhill.

CHAPEL OPEN: at house opening times, as advertised

EDENSOR St Peter (Grade I)

SK 251 699

The village - gated and walled - is utterly fascinating, being the result of an arbitrary re-siting of the community by the 6th Duke of Devonshire, who no longer wished to see the old houses from the windows of Chatsworth! The main work was carried out under Sir Joseph Paxton (of Crystal Palace fame) between 1838 and 1842, with houses, shops, stables, etc. designed in every conceivable architectural style. Eventually the parish church also was rebuilt in 1867 (but on its old site) to a magnificent design by Sir George Gilbert Scott. Retained from the earlier building was the vast C17 Baroque monument to William (1st Earl) and Henry Cavendish (both sons of Bess of Hardwick), now occupying the entire west wall of the family chapel to the south of the chancel. Also in the church is a plaque commemorating a visit by

19

President Kennedy, whose sister, married to one of the family, died in an air crash and is buried in the churchyard. Another tomb is that of Joseph Paxton, architectural designer, and one-time Head Gardener at Chatsworth.

SUNDAY SERVICE: 10.30
CHURCH OPEN: daily, 9.00 till dusk
COFFEE MORNING: Tues 10.00-12.00 (summer)
EDENSOR DAY: nearest Sat to St Peter's Day (29 June)
CONTACT: (01246) 582130 (Vicar)
P D ⚚ ♦

EYAM St Lawrence, Church Street
SK 218 764

The C13 church, with later additions and Victorian restorations, is probably best known for its connections with the 1665-66 plague - a terrible event recalled in both church and village by numerous memorials and other reminders. The story of how Parson Mompesson quarantined the village to prevent the spread of the disease is fully documented in the church exhibition. From a much earlier era is the finely carved Saxon cross - claimed to be one of the best in England - in the churchyard, just south of the chancel.

SUNDAY SERVICES: 8.00, 10.30, 6.15
CHURCH OPEN: daily, 9.00-6.00 (Easter to October) 9.00-4.00 (winter)
WELL DRESSING & PLAGUE COMMEMORATION SERVICE: last w/e October
CONTACT: (01433) 630930 (Administrator) - NB Visiting school parties must make a booking
Publications: guide books in seven European languages
P (public CP) D ▢ ♿

FOOLOW St Hugh
SK 191 768

A tiny Victorian Gothic building of 1888. It faces a large pond and green in the middle of a small, picturesque limestone village whose houses date mostly from the C18 and C19.

SUNDAY SERVICES: 9.30 (2nd only), 3.15
CHURCH OPEN: daily, 10.30 till dusk (summer)
WELL DRESSING: last Sun August
P

GREAT LONGSTONE St Giles, Church Lane (Grade I)

SK 200 719

Most of what we see is of C14 and C15 - all very sensitively restored by Norman Shaw in 1873. It is perhaps the woodwork that is most worthy of notice: the C15 ceilings and bosses of nave, aisles and chancel, together with Shaw's sympathetic furnishings in the form of stalls, organ case and pulpit. At the east end of the south aisle is the Lady Chapel, formerly known as the Hassop Pew on account of its connection with the Eyre family of that place.

SUNDAY SERVICES: 11.00, 6.30
CHURCH OPEN: daily, 9.00-6.00
FLOWER FESTIVAL: end May for week
Publication: J N Tarn, "St Giles Great Longstone"
P (street) ♟ ♿ wc

Saxon Cross, Eyam

GRINDLEFORD St Helen, Sheffield Road

SK 242 778

The church presents a curious aspect when viewed from the road. The imposing chancel and side chapel, both of 1910, must have been intended as the beginning of a quite ambitious structure. Clearly the project was cut short in its prime - probably on account of the Great War - and the nave was later completed in a more utilitarian manner. Worth looking at, though, for the sake of the chancel and its well designed ensemble of furnishings.

SUNDAY SERVICE: 9.30
KEY AVAILABLE: at Post Office (over bridge)
P (street) [wc]

HADDON HALL Private Chapel

SK 235 664

In former times this was also the parish church of Nether Haddon. The original chapel was part of the C12 house; it was enlarged with the addition of aisles in the C14 and the present chancel was completed in 1427. C15 wall paintings are still visible and there are no furnishings later than C17.

CHAPEL OPEN: at Hall opening times, as advertised

HASSOP All Saints Chapel (RC)

SK 223 724

Built 1816/1818 as a private chapel for the Eyre family of Hassop Hall, this is an exquisite Classical Revival temple with an impressive pillared portico in the Etruscan style and a barrel vaulted interior. The ornate altar and reredos is said to be of French origin. In the back gallery is a gem of a chamber organ by H C Lincoln dating from the 1820's and recently restored.

SUNDAY MASS: 9.00 (1st), 10.30 (other Suns)
CHURCH OPEN: daily
CONTACT: (01629) 640241 (Presbytery)
P (in road) 🕯 ♿

HOPE St Peter (Grade I)

SK 172 834

Embattled aisles, clerestory and porch indicate a systematic rebuild during the Perpendicular period. There are C13c memorials with the symbols of forest officers (or "woodroffes"). Other interesting furnishings include a 1652 pulpit and stall backs made from C17 pews. A C18 painting is of Moses and Aaron. As at nearby Castleton there is a copy of the "Breeches" Bible.

SUNDAY SERVICE: 9.30 (1st, 2nd, 3rd), 10.45 (4th), joint with other churches (5th)
CHURCH OPEN: Sat morning (summer)
OPEN FOR WAKES WEEK: last week June/ 1st week July
P (street or public CP)

All Saints Chapel, Hassop

OVER HADDON
St Anne

SK 204 664

The limestone village, with a population of about 250, clings to the side of a steep slope, giving glorious views over Lathkill Dale - views which may perhaps be best enjoyed from the churchyard. The church itself is a small Gothic structure of 1880; a pretty, gilded sundial was erected on the south wall of the chancel in 1977.

SUNDAY SERVICE: 9.30 (2nd, 4th & 5th), 11.00 (1st & 3rd)
CHURCH OPEN: daily, 8.30-5.30
P (public CP 50yds)

PADLEY Padley Chapel (RC), Upper Padley (Grade I)

SK 247 789

This historic Chapel is reached on foot via a rough track, over the bridge from Grindleford Station (about half a mile). It is above the C15 gatehouse, all that survives intact of Padley Hall, home of a branch of the Fitzherbert family who supported the Catholic cause during the persecution years of the C16. The Chapel was restored in 1933 to commemorate the arrest in 1588 of two priests hidden in the house. Amidst the ruins to the north of the Chapel is now an open air altar around which a large pilgrimage mass takes place each year to celebrate the martyrs.

ANNUAL PILGRIMAGE: Sun nearest to 12 July
CHAPEL OPEN: Sun & Wed from 2.00
CONTACT: (01433) 630572
Publications: C Fitzherbert, "Padley, A Short History . . . "
also pictorial guide booklet, "Look at Padley",
published by joint churches in Hathersage
P (Grindleford Station)

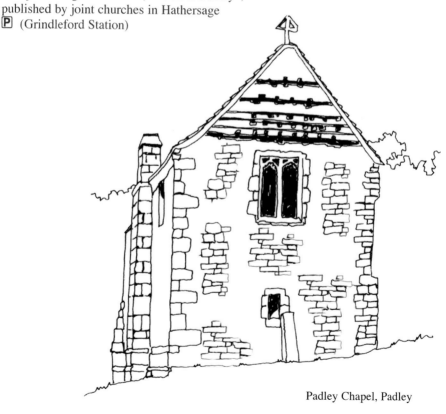

Padley Chapel, Padley

St Michael & All Angels, Sheldon

SHELDON St Michael & All Angels

SK 175 689

Small Gothic church of c1865 with bellcote and apsidal chancel. The Great War made a deep impression on Sheldon: five names are recorded on the War Memorial, including that of Tony Gyte whose mother, Maria, kept a detailed and moving diary of both local and international happenings during that troubled period.

SUNDAY SERVICE: 9.00 (2nd & 4th only)
CHURCH OPEN: daily, 9.00-6.00
Publication: G Phizackerley, "The Diaries of Maria Gyte of Sheldon, Derbyshire 1913-1920"
(also published by Scarthin Books, Cromford)
P (street)

WARDLOW Good Shepherd

SK 182 747

Small church of 1873 in Perpendicular Gothic style. Joined to it, making an overall T-plan, is the schoolroom with a double bellcote at the junction.

SUNDAY SERVICE: 9.45 (1st & 3rd only)
CHURCH OPEN: daily, 9.00-6.00
P (street) WC

BELPER & DUFFIELD

BELPER Central Methodist, Chapel Street

SK 347 473

Built in 1807, this listed building is the largest surviving pre-Victorian chapel in the county. It is square in plan, as favoured by the early Wesleyans, with a hipped roof. The gallery still retains its original seating and there is a a fine plaster ceiling. Construction is of stone with square sash windows; the style is plain save for the pedimented front. The building is set back from the A6 in its own large graveyard, now a pleasant garden. When first built the chapel was described as "the wonder of the country for many miles around" on account of its great size (accommodating 1,400 people - so it was said!). It is now a listed building and there are plans for its restoration.

SUNDAY SERVICES: 10.45, 6.15
CHURCH OPEN (coffee): Fri 10.00-12.00 + some Sats
OPEN FOR FLOWER FESTIVAL (2nd Thur June till following Sun)
PREMISES OPEN: Mon - Thur 10.00-12.00 - usually somebody available
CONTACT: (01773) 823581 (Mrs Briggs)
P (church CP to rear) WC

BELPER Christ Church, Bridge Street

SK 345 479

Built in 1850 to a design by H I Stevens, it is a large, aisleless hall without architectural division at the chancel or sanctuary. A major restoration and refurbishment was completed for the Millennium. Its superb acoustics and open layout make it a popular venue for musical concerts.

SUNDAY SERVICES: 7.45, 11.00, 6.30
CHURCH OPEN: daily
P (at rear) WC

Central Methodist, Belper

BELPER St John's Chapel (Heritage Centre), St John's Road

SK 353 475

A simple 13th century chapel for the mediaeval hamlet of Belper, originally coming under the extensive parish of Duffield. Following the industrial growth of Belper the chapel's function was necessarily replaced by the large 1824 church of St Peter's. The building is now divided into two sections, the west end being used as a Town Council Chamber while the remainder is a heritage centre and meeting room for local societies.

HERITAGE CENTRE OPEN: Mon (ex bh), Tue, Wed, Fri, 9.30-12.30
CONTACT: (01773) 822116
Publication: E G Power, "St. John's Chapel, Belper"
P 🗋 ⬛ ♿ wc

BELPER St Peter, Chesterfield Road

SK 351 477

This large, Gothic "Commissioners" church, built in 1824 to replace the old St John's Chapel (see above), enjoys a commanding hillside position. Tree-lined avenues lead through the churchyard towards the tall, slender tower (now unfortunately shorn of its pinnacle tops) which is a prominent landmark on the Belper skyline. With a wide, rectangular nave, shallow sanctuary and large gallery at back and sides, the building remains structurally unaltered. In the west gallery stands the historic 3-manual organ by Holt (1853, enlarged 1873 and recently restored).

SUNDAY SERVICES: 8.00, 10.30, 6.30
CHURCH & OFFICE OPEN: Tue-Fri, 10.00-12.00
CONTACT: (01773) 828772 (during above office hours) or (01773) 822148 (Vicar)
P (Chesterfield Rd or public CP) 🗋 ♀ wc

BELPER Unitarian, Field Row (off Green Lane)

SK 350 479

Built in 1788 by local mill owner, Jedediah Strutt, and enlarged with side wings in about 1800. The interior has steeply tiered box pews rising towards each side and there is a small rear gallery with access only from an exterior cantilevered stone staircase. Among the family monuments is one to Jedediah Strutt, 1797, "Founder of this Chapel". There is also a late 18th century octagonal pulpit. Entered from outside is a "catacomb" in which are interred several members of the Strutt family.

SUNDAY SERVICE: 3.00 (1st & 3rd)
CONTACT: (01773) 824946
Publication: D Smith, "Belper Unitarian Chapel"
Ⓟ (in Green Lane)   🚪   ♿

DUFFIELD Evangelical Baptist, Town Street

SK 346 429

Built as a General Baptist Chapel in 1830, with a schoolroom added in 1877. The north facade and the west side, both facing the A6 road across an attractive graveyard, are of red brick with nicely detailed stone dressings. The interior has a congregational gallery over the porch and one for the choir and organ behind the pulpit.

SUNDAY SERVICES: 10.45, 6.30
"OPEN DOORS": Tues 11.00-12.30   ("sit & pray - coffee & chat - or just look round")
CHURCH OFFICE: (01332) 843011
Brochure: "Time for Change"
Ⓟ (adjacent)   🚪   🚻

DUFFIELD St Alkmund (Grade I)

SK 349 428

The church contains substantial work ranging from the 12th to the 19th centuries. Though only three bays long the nave has very broad north and south aisles, thus giving an overall width that is greater than the nave's length. A north transept (adding even more to the width of the nave), originally a chapel, contains the fine, early 17th century monument to Anthony Bradshaw, his two wives and twenty children. Church facilities were enhanced in 1992 by the addition of a small cloister on the south side across which is the new church hall - a fine piece of sympathetic modern design by the local architect, Anthony Rossi.

SUNDAY SERVICES: 10.00, 6.30
CHURCH OPEN: daily
Publication: "The Parish Church of St. Alkmund Duffield"
Ⓟ   🚪   ♿   🚻 (when church hall is open)

HOLBROOK St Michael

SK 364 446

Holbrook village occupies a high site on a ridge between the Derwent and the Bottle Brook, with good views over the latter towards the spire of Horsley church. St Michael's originated as a small C18 chapel in the parish of Duffield, becoming a parochial centre in its own right about a hundred years later. It was enlarged (in Classical style with Inigo Jones overtones) in 1841 and further rebuilt and enlarged in 1907-8 following a fire. Particularly effective (albeit alien to the overall style) is the large, semicircular east window with its Art Nouveau tracery, dating from the latter rebuild. An annual event in the village is the ecumenical procession of Christian Witness on 1st Sunday in July.

SUNDAY SERVICES: 9.00, 10.45, 6.30
CONTACT: (01332) 880442 (Mr Styles) P (street) ♿ WC

Tomb of Sir John and Lady Curzon, All Saints, Kedleston

KEDLESTON All Saints (Grade I)

SK 312 403

The church stands next to Kedleston Hall and is administered by the National Trust for the Redundant Churches Fund. It is cruciform with a central tower, Norman in origin though mostly of the C13. The sumptuous north nave aisle was designed by G F Bodley in 1907 to house the memorial to the wife of Lord Curzon, Viceroy of India. Other Curzon monuments in the church go back to the C13.

CHURCH OPEN: at Hall opening times, as advertised by National Trust

LITTLE EATON St Paul

SK 363 415

Little Eaton occupies the low ground at the confluence of the Bottle Brook and the Derwent. The church was built in 1791 and enlarged in 1837, but it is the "Normanization" of 1869 which is now its dominant characteristic. The arms of George III on display in the church reflect the date of its origin. Monuments to two former incumbents include that of Canon Latham, founder of the Derby Diocesan Training College for Schoolmistresses.

SUNDAY SERVICES: 8.00, 10.30, 6.30
CONTACT: list of key holders advertised on notice board
P (street)

MUGGINTON Halter Devil Chapel

SK 271 449

A curious little Classical chapel of 1723 attached to a farmhouse. It has a stylish, stone-faced facade though the other walls are plain and simple, as is the interior. Visitors are recommended to read for themselves the story of how a farmer, late at night, swore he would ride into Derby even if he had to "halter the Devil". On trying to halter his own horse he found it had horns!

KEY AVAILABLE: at adjoining farmhouse

Halter Devil Chapel, Mugginton

BOLSOVER & STAVELEY

AULT HUCKNALL St John the Baptist (Grade I)

SK 467 652

An ambitious cruciform church in miniature within what has been described as "the smallest village in England"; a large part of the parish, however, is taken up by the grounds and estate of Hardwick Hall. There are substantial amounts of masonry, notably the west front, north arcade and eastern arch of the crossing, which are of Saxon or very early Norman origin. Particularly worthy of note is the carved tympanum (over the blocked up west door) displaying an Agnus Dei together with St Margaret emerging from the body of the Devil(!). At the east end of the south aisle is some 1527 glass depicting the Crucifixion. Below the elaborate 1627 monument to Anne Keighley (wife of 1st Earl of Devonshire) is a slab to Thomas Hobbes, the philosopher, who died at Hardwick in 1679.

SUNDAY SERVICE: 11.00
CHURCH OPEN: Sat 1.00-5.00 (Easter to Harvest)
WELL DRESSING: 3rd Sat July for week
CONTACT: (01246) 850371 (Incumbent)
P 🚪 ♦ wc

CRESSWELL St Mary Magdalene, Elmton Road

SK 526 743

A spacious church, built in 1899-1900 for the Duke of Portland and designed by L Ambler; aisles were added in 1914 and the tower in 1927 - all still by Ambler. Two particularly fine features are the memorial window to the 1950 Cresswell Colliery disaster and the rose window at the east end. In the churchyard are many graves from the 1950 disaster.

SUNDAY SERVICES: 8.30, 9.30, 6.00
CONTACT: (01909) 721264 (Vicar)
P (street for 30 mins or public CP 50 yds) wc

ECKINGTON St Peter & St Paul, Church Street (Grade I)

SK 432 798

This is one of Derbyshire's greater churches and one that certainly should be better known. It contains important work of each century from the twelfth to the twentieth, though it is probably that of the earliest period which will demand our closest attention. On arrival the visitor will be impressed by the massive, flat buttressed tower, whose west door is still round Norman while its belfry windows are of the simplest early lancet Gothic; all this is surmounted by a large C14 stone spire. Once inside we cannot fail to notice the tall C12 Norman arcades with five bays apiece, of which the three easternmost each side are slightly earlier. Even the C18 has been allowed to leave its mark in the form of the south aisle wall and porch - though the former Georgian chancel was clearly just too much for the 1907 re-Gothicisers to bear!. The church contains several monuments of the Sitwell family (from nearby Renishaw Hall), one of whom brought back from Italy the altar painting (after Annibale Carracci).

SUNDAY SERVICES: 9.30, 6.30
CHURCH OPEN: Fri, Sat, Sun, 2.00-4.00 (Easter to Harvest)
CONTACT: (01246) 432196 (Rector)
Publication: P Bond, "A History of St Peter and St Paul Church, Eckington"
P (street or White Hart CP)   📖   ♛

ELMTON St Peter

SK 502 735

C18 churches are few and far between in Derbyshire. This one is the result of a total rebuild in 1771 of a mediaeval church. It has a nave, and low, apsed chancel, together with an incomplete west tower. A carved pulpit and tester are of the same date. In the church hangs a painting of Jedidiah Buxton, the C18 arithmetical genius, whose home was in Elmton.

SUNDAY SERVICE: 11.00
WELL DRESSING: last w/e June
KEY AVAILABLE: from Elmtree Inn
P (street)

KILLAMARSH St Giles, Kirkcroft Lane

SK 461 810

The village is right in the north east corner of the county, adjacent to Sheffield. The church was enlarged and restored in the late C19, though a fine Norman south doorway still remains. A C15 window in the chancel of Virgin (crowned) and Child was recently conserved and repaired by the York Glaziers' Trust. In the churchyard are a Saxon cross and the restored Parish stocks.

SUNDAY SERVICES: 8.30 10.00
CONTACT: (0114) 248 2769 (Rector) or (0114) 248 2734 (Mr Whitfield)
Publication: R J Bradshaw, "The Parish Church of St Giles"
P (street or cemetery, 50 yds)

PLEASLEY St Michael

SK 504 645

Norman origins are clear in the chancel arch and font. As for the rest it consists of aisleless nave and chancel, all dating from the C13.

SUNDAY SERVICE: 9.30
CONTACT: (01623) 810574 (Mr Clay)
FLOWER FESTIVAL: 2nd Sun July for 5 days
P

RENISHAW St Matthew

SK 447 778

This Gothic church was opened in 1903 as a Chapel of Ease in Eckington parish. Of simple design, "it always has a neat and well kept appearance".

SUNDAY SERVICE: 9.30
CHURCH OPEN: Tue mornings (coffee)
P (street)

RIDGEWAY St John the Evangelist, Main Road

SK 402 812

An 1840's Gothic church with a later C19 tower. The chancel has now been refurbished as a small worship area, while the nave and aisles have been converted into a hall and meeting rooms - a good example of how an unwieldy Victorian building can be effectively adapted to modern needs.

SUNDAY SERVICE: 10.45
CONTACT: (01246) 433666 (Mrs Farrer)
P (street) 🕮 wc

STAVELEY Methodist, Chesterfield Road

SK 430 746

Opened in 1976 this is an integral complex consisting of church, schoolrooms and hall. It is of brick finish, both outside and in, with window layout of similar design to that of Coventry Cathedral. Organ, pulpit and full-sized stone font (unusual in the Methodist tradition) are all from the previous Wesleyan chapel on the site.

SUNDAY SERVICES:
10.30 & (occasionally)
3.00 (GMT) or 6.00
(BST)
"OPEN DOORS"
(coffee): Fri 10.30-11.30
- refreshments - sit &
pray - or just look round
P ☕ ♿ wc

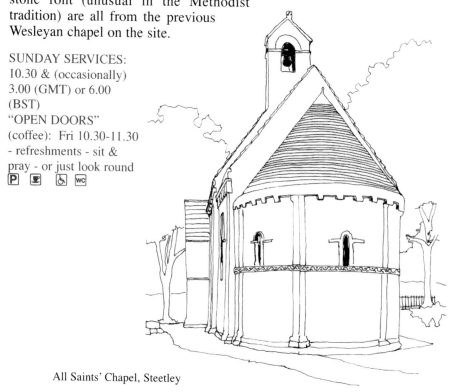

All Saints' Chapel, Steetley

STAVELEY Poolsbrook Methodist, Cottage Close

SK 443 734

Built in 1893, this chapel is within the Bolsover & Staveley Circuit. Visitors are welcome to have a look round.

SUNDAY SERVICE: 3.00
CONTACT: (01246) 477993
P 🕿 wc

STEETLEY All Saints' Chapel (Grade I)

SK 543 787

Though tiny and necessarily restored, this is a priceless gem dating from the mid 12th century. It is tri-cellular - nave, chancel and apsed sanctuary. By the C19 the chapel was ruinous and roofless, so much of what we see is due to J L Pearson's tasteful restoration of 1876-80, of which the vaulting of the apse is particularly effective. The atmosphere of the interior is nowadays enhanced by visitor-operated lighting on a time switch. The parish of Whitwell (see below), to which the chapel belongs, is indeed blessed in having two such outstanding Norman places of worship.

SUNDAY SERVICE: 3.15
CHURCH OPEN: daily, 9.00-6.00
Publication: "All Saints Steetley"
CONTACT: (01909) 720220 (Rector)
P 🗋 ♿

UPPER LANGWITH (or LANGWITH BASSETT) Holy Cross

SK 519 614

A simple nave and chancel of C13 origin and C15 appearance. The pretty bellcote was added by Norman Shaw at his restoration in 1877.

SUNDAY SERVICE: 10.00
CONTACT: (01623) 743379 (Mrs Launders)
FLOWER FESTIVAL & WELL DRESSING: early July
Publication: G Bevan, "A History of Langwith Bassett"
P 🗋

WHITWELL St Lawrence, High Street (Grade I)

SK 526 769

After Melbourne this must be the most impressive Norman nave in the county, with tower arch, north and south arcades, an especially fine chancel arch and even (unusually, since they have not been enlarged at a later date) the clerestory window openings - all pure 12th century Norman. The 14th century saw the addition of the transepts and the enlarging of the chancel, the latter being particularly spacious, with a finely preserved sedilia. Interesting glass is to be found in both transepts - in the south are windows saved from St James, Derby, while the C14 so-called "Monkey" windows are in the traceries of the north one.

SUNDAY SERVICES: 8.15, 9.30, plus 6.00 (1st only)
CHURCH OPEN: Mon-Fri, 8.45-5.15
CONTACT: (01909) 720220
(Rector)

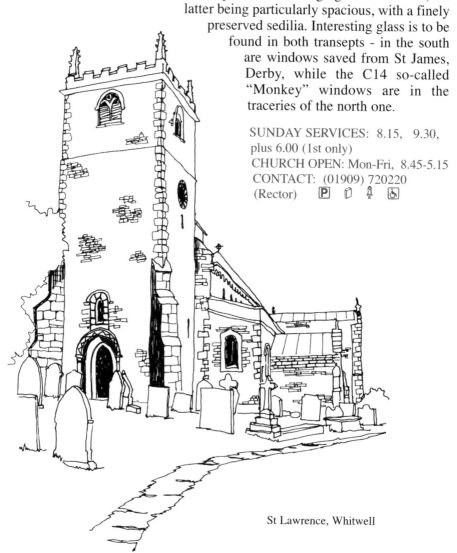

St Lawrence, Whitwell

BUXTON & TIDESWELL

BUXTON Methodist, Eagle Parade (Market Place)

SK 057 732

Built in 1849 this is a rare, early example of non-conformist Gothic - not just a few, plainly pointed windows but a stylish essay by J Wilson (Bath) in Puginesque 14th century Decorated style. The "churchy" character is further enhanced by the later 19th century addition of transepts and chancel. Following a major re-roofing operation the interior was refurbished during the 1980's and 90's with tasteful modern fittings and furnishings; this resulted in a Civic Association award in 1994. The 3-manual organ by Alexander Young, installed in 1895, remains a fine and well-preserved example of that firm's work.

SUNDAY SERVICES: 11.00, 6.30
CHURCH & PREMISES OPEN: Tue & Sat mornings
CHURCH OFFICE: (01298) 27075
Publications: "The Story . . . So Far" (this and a number of other booklets are produced by their own "Church in the Market Place Publications")
[P] (street nearby)   [.]   [*] (Tue & Sat mornings)   [&] [wc]

BUXTON St Anne (RC), Terrace Road

SK 059 735

The present church dates from 1861 and is in the lancet style of Gothic.

SUNDAY MASS: 8.30, 11.00
CHURCH OPEN: mornings, 9.30-10.30
CONTACT: (01298) 23777 (Presbytery)
[P] [.] [wc]

CHAPEL-EN-LE-FRITH St Thomas Becket, Market Place

SK 057 808

The church is an interesting mixture of Gothic and Classical. It is a large, aisled structure dating mostly from the C14, but the tower and south elevation of the nave were reclothed in round-arched Classical style during the 1730's. The most important features of the interior are the furnishings - C15 font, C17 altar rails (now at the back), C18 organ case and the complete set of box pews of 1831. In the chancel is the tomb of The Revd William Bagshawe, "The Apostle of the Peak".

SUNDAY SERVICES: 8.00, 10.30, 6.30
CHURCH OPEN: Thur 10.00-12.00
CONTACT: (01298) 812134 (Vicar)
P (street) 🚻 👥 ♿ wc

CHAPEL-EN-LE-FRITH Town End Methodist, Market Street

SK 062 808

Listed former Wesleyan chapel dating from 1874; stone building with small spire and graveyard to rear. A porch and coffee lounge were added in 1994 and the interior modernized, the original balcony being retained. The adjacent former Sunday School building has been converted to housing.

SUNDAY SERVICE: 10.30
CHURCH OPEN: Sat 10.00-12.00 (coffee) & Thu 8.00pm-9.30pm ("Drop-In")
CONTACT: (01298) 816272 (Minister)
P 👥(Sat) ♿ wc

CHELMORTON St John the Baptist

SK 116 702

Said to be the highest churchyard in Derbyshire - 1,200 feet above sea level. The church is at the top end of a one-street village; it has an aisled nave, chancel (with sedilia) and large south transept (built as a chantry), all of C13 and C14. The fine stone rood screen is of about 1345 with a wooden top section added in the C20.. Other interior items of interest include a parish chest (1630) and charity boards, while outside there is a locust (symbol of John the Baptist) weather vane atop the spire and an Elizabethan porch made of coffin lids.

SUNDAY SERVICE: 11.30
CHURCH OPEN: daily, 9.30-5.00 (summer)
CHELMORTON FESTIVAL: 3rd week June
CONTACT: (01298) 85348 (Mr Mosley)
P (street)

COMBS Methodist, Lesser Lane

SK 042 784

Built in 1864, about 3 miles SW of Chapel-en-le-Frith and situated in a picturesque valley near to Combs Reservoir where there is yachting and fishing. With the help of the Combs Village Hall Trust, local fund-raising and grants from various bodies, the premises have now been restored and extended as a combined venture, the official re-opening having been in 1998.

SUNDAY SERVICE: 2.45 (1st & 3rd only)
CONTACT: (01298) 816272 (Minister) or (01298) 812459
🅿 ♿ 🚾

CRESSBROOK St John the Evangelist

SK 167 733

This church, built in 1877, needs to be seen as part of an interesting ensemble - that of a model village for the workers at the magnificent mill in the Wye valley below. The community is set amidst trees on a steep hillside, the terraces of cottages and the other buildings being designed in a pretty Tudor style. The church has an apse and contains carved wooden furnishings by Advent Hunstone of Tideswell.

SUNDAY SERVICE: 9.00 (2nd & 4th only)
CONTACT: (01298) 871214 (Mr Stafford)
OPEN FOR WELL DRESSING: June (date as advertised)
🅿 (street - limited) ⚲ ♿ 🚾

FAIRFIELD St Peter

SK 067 742

The church enjoys a most attractive location by Fairfield Common on the northern (A6) approach to Buxton. The first building on the site was a small mediaeval chapel. This was replaced in 1839 by the present nave and tower. Further extension followed with transepts and chancel in 1902, resulting in what is now quite an extensive church. An interesting World War I memorial window contains (for the first time in an English window) a picture of an aeroplane. The organ is a fine 1893 instrument by Conacher.

SUNDAY SERVICES: 8.00, 10.00
CONTACT: (01298) 23629 (Vicar)
🅿 ♿ 🚾

LITTON Christ Church, Church Lane
SK 163 754

The church, though comparatively modern (1927), is in a traditional style using local materials and harmonizes well with the pretty village. With the exception of an C18 font the fittings are all designed by the architect of the church, W H R Blacking; particularly worthy of note are the roof bosses and the rood beam with its figures.

SUNDAY SERVICE: 10.00 (1st & 3rd only)
CONTACT: (01298) 871740 (Mrs Barber)
OPEN FOR WELL DRESSING: June, concurrently with Tideswell (qv)
🅿 (street)

St John the Baptist, Tideswell

MILLER'S DALE St Anne

SK 142 734

A neat little church of simple nave and tower in Perpendicular Gothic style dating from 1879. Together with its small community, it is on the hillside close to the river which runs through the Dale bearing its same name, and is overshadowed by the two great iron railway viaducts (at present disused). As in some other churches around Tideswell, there are fine wood carvings by Advent Hunstone; the church also possesses some embroidery by William Morris.

SUNDAY SERVICE: 9.00 (1st & 3rd only)
CONTACT: (01298) 872669 (Mr Monk)
P (limited)

MONYASH St Leonard, Church Street

SK 151 665

A fairly large limestone church with aisles and transepts. From the Norman period survive the magnificent sedilia and piscina with their dogtoothed segmental arches. Most of the rest appears to be C13 and C14, though Butterfield's restoration of 1887 included the total rebuilding of the north transept; Butterfield was also responsible for the rich encaustic floor tiles and the finely carved roof trusses and pews.

SUNDAY SERVICE: 8.45 (1st & 3rd), 10.00 (2nd & 4th)
CHURCH OPEN: daily, 9.30-5.00 (summer)
CONTACT: (01629) 812234 (Vicar)
P (street)

TADDINGTON St Michael, Main Street (Grade I)

SK 141 712

Taddington, at 1,000 feet above sea level, can still be looked down upon most spectacularly as one ascends the Monyash road south of the village. The present church largely dates from 1373 and therefore presents a harmonious architectural ensemble in the early Perpendicular Gothic style. The tall straight-headed windows of the chancel reflect a similar style and period to that of Tideswell. Items of interest include two mediaeval stone fonts, a Jacobean pulpit and the C17/18 fresco in the nave.

SUNDAY SERVICE: 10.00
CHURCH OPEN: daily, 9.00-5.00
CONTACT: (01298) 85203 (M Elkington)
P (street)

TIDESWELL St John the Baptist (Grade I)

SK 152 758

Popularly referred to as "The Cathedral of the Peak" on account of both its size and its cathedral-like cruciform plan. Chesterfield may be larger and Melbourne may be older, but this must surely be the most beautiful, architecturally speaking, of Derbyshire's larger churches - a factor due (as at Taddington, above) to its homogeneity of design. It was built (or, more correctly, rebuilt), without major breaks, over the years c1340 to c1400, the tower alone being completed later. Features of interest are too numerous for the present coverage: suffice to comment on the gloriously spacious chancel - almost as long as the nave - and the fine Gothic organ case and other woodwork in the north transept carved by Advent Hunstone. Recommended to the interested visitor are the numerous guides and histories on sale - many written by the present incumbent, Canon Martin Hulbert.

SUNDAY SERVICE: 10.00
CHURCH OPEN: daily, dawn till dusk
WELL DRESSING & WAKES: from Sat nearest 24 June
Publications: M Hulbert, "The Cathedral of the Peak", "The Woodcarvings at Tideswell", "The Windows at Tideswell", etc., etc.
CONTACT: (01298) 871317 (Vicar) or (01298) 871526 (Administrator)
P (street) 🕯 ♨ ♿ WC (in Institute)

CHESTERFIELD

BARLOW (or GREAT BARLOW) St Lawrence

SK 345 746

This is essentially a small church serving a rural community. It consists of Norman nave and chancel with an extended neo-Norman east end added in 1867.

SUNDAY SERVICES: 11.00
CHURCH OPEN: weekends (summer)
OPEN FOR WELL DRESSING: 2nd week August
CONTACT: (0114) 2890310 (Churchwarden)
P (street) wc

BRAMPTON St Mark, St Mark's Road, off Springfield Avenue

SK 371 712

A 1940 urban red brick church, uninvitingly plain from the outside, but surprisingly pleasant once you enter - the vista towards the sanctuary being particularly effective. A new wooden floor (happily not covered by carpeting) helps generate the kind of acoustics which, aided by an effective, small modern organ, create an atmosphere that is very conducive to worship.

SUNDAY SERVICES: 8.00, 10.00
CONTACT: (01246) 234015 (Vicar)
P (street) & wc

BRAMPTON St Thomas, Chatsworth Road

SK 363 706

The church started as a fairly conventional Commissioners' building of 1832. A very spacious chancel was added in 1888. The chief quality of the interior is that, although wide, it is open and free of pillars, with a large, strikingly painted ceiling. A major refurbishment has taken place during 1998/99. The organ is a large and impressive Romantic instrument by Lloyd (1906). In the churchyard a peaceful garden of remembrance has recently been created.

SUNDAY SERVICES: 9.00, 11.00, 6.30
CHURCH OPEN: Mon-Fri 9.00-12.30 & 2.00-4.00 (ex Wed pm) : access via office, at east end
CHURCH OFFICE: (01246) 558461
P (rear of church) 🅟 🕴 (office staff will assist/advise) [wc]

CHESTERFIELD Annunciation (RC), Spencer Street
SK 380 716

The architect was J A Hansom (of Hansom Cab fame) and the church was opened in 1854 by the Jesuit Fathers of Mount St Mary's, Spinkhill. The tower-like west end structure, Germanic in style, was added in 1874, shortly after which the fine and well-preserved "Father" Willis organ was installed in the new west gallery. The church contains a wealth of 19th and 20th century stained glass.

SUNDAY MASS: 8.00 9.30 11.00, 7.00
CONTACT: (01246) 232686 (Presbytery, next door)
P (limited amount at rear, via Queen's Street) 🅟 [wc] (in Parish Centre)

CHESTERFIELD Central Methodist, Saltergate
SK 384 713

The large and impressive building dates from 1870 - a period of supreme non-conformist self-confidence. It is in Palladian style with a projecting portico, full height, with pediment and giant Ionic columns. The formerly galleried interior has recently been gutted and modernized - very tastefully, though one regrets the loss of the fine pipe organ. As part of the refurbishment the chapel floor level was raised allowing rooms (including a coffee shop) to be built underneath.

SUNDAY SERVICES:
ACCESS TO CHURCH: via coffee shop, on request

CHESTERFIELD Elder Yard Unitarian, Elder Way

SK 383 712

This, the oldest surviving non-conformist chapel in Derbyshire - built in 1694 and originally Independent - is of the type (like the slightly later Chinley Chapel) that would have had the pulpit in the middle of the long side. Two refurbishments during the 19th century have resulted in it being re-orientated to the now more common longitudinal arrangement. The style of the exterior is pleasantly domestic in the late 17th century manner, with rusticated quoins and large mullion-and-transom windows. The setting is within a pleasantly leafy graveyard some of whose stones date from as early as the 1690's, with Chesterfield's captains of industry well represented.

SUNDAY SERVICE: 3.00 (fortnightly)
CHAPEL OPEN: mornings, Mon-Fri & all day Sat
OTHER OPEN EVENTS: Sat coffee 9.30-12.00 & monthly Sat concert 12.15-1.00
CHAPEL OFFICE: (01246) 559407 (answerphone out of normal open hours)
Publication: D W Robson (revised A W Vallance), "The Story of Elder Yard Unitarian Chapel Chesterfield"
P (Holywell Cross public CP - 2 minutes' walk)   ⓘ 🖼 (Sat) ♿ wc

Elder Yard Unitarian, Chesterfield

CHESTERFIELD Holy Trinity, Newbold Road

SK 384 698

A "Commissioners'"-style church of 1838 with later C19 alterations. The Victorian interior was re-ordered and modernized in 1994. The stained glass in the east window is a memorial (1848) to George Stephenson, the railway engineer, who is buried in the church.

SUNDAY SERVICES: 10.30, 6.30
CONTACT: (01246) 273508 (Vicar)
Ⓟ (public CP) 🛈 ♿ 🚻

CHESTERFIELD St Mary & All Saints, St Mary's Gate (Grade A)

SK 385 712

With its famous "crooked" spire this is the largest church building in Derbyshire, cruciform in plan and dating mostly from the 13th and 14th centuries. The spire ("twisted" is perhaps a better word for it) was added about 1400, is 228 feet high and, at its apex, leans as much as nine feet out of true. The importance of the church and town in the middle ages is reflected in the multiplicity of guild chapels at the east end of the choir and transepts. Some blackened interior stonework still reminds us of the 1961 fire in the north transept which destroyed the historic Snetzler organ.

SUNDAY SERVICES: 8.00, 10.30, 6.30
CHURCH OPEN: daily, 9.00-5.30
CONTACT: (01246) 206506 (Verger)
Gift shop: 10.00-4.00 (NB foreign language guides in preparation)
Coffee shop "The Saints" (to south of churchyard, in St Mary's Gate): 10.00-4.00 (not Wed or Sun)
Publications: various
Ⓟ (public CP's nearby) 🖊 🖼 ♿ 🚻 (in coffee shop)

CLAY CROSS St Bartholomew, High Street

SK 391 633

By H I Stevens, 1851, with a tall broach-spire visible over a wide area. The site offers good views westwards over the Amber Valley and Ogston Reservoir. In the south aisle is some Victorian glass to a Burne-Jones design representing Saints John, Peter and James. Out in the churchyard there is the ancient base of a stone cross after which the town was named.

SUNDAY SERVICES: 10.00, 6.00
CONTACT: (01246) 851193 (Miss Hamblin) or (01246) 866021 (Verger)
OPEN FOR MINI-MARKET: 1st Sat June, 9.00-11.00
Ⓟ 🖊 ♿ 🚻

St Mary & All Saints, Chesterfield

DRONFIELD St John the Baptist, Church Street (Grade I)

SK 353 783

This must be one of the least well known of the great churches in our County. What we have is a church of Norman origin transformed on a grand scale during the C14 and C15. The glory, of course, is the great chancel - slightly earlier than that of Tideswell: early C14 and still in Decorated Gothic style. What is sad is that, soon after the Reformation, the chancel became ruinous and the tracery of the enormous east window fell out and was replaced by straight-line vertical and horizontal bars. Even so, there is still some C14 glass in one of the south windows, a C14 sedilia and choir stalls (with misericords) dating from the C15. Of a later date is the altar reredos carved by Advent Hunstone of Tideswell in 1907. In the nave is a fine Jacobean pulpit and there are over 120 monumental brasses, the earliest being of a Rector and Chantry Priest (1399).

SUNDAY SERVICES: 8.00, 9.30, 11.15, 6.30
CHURCH OPEN: daily
Publication: "Dronfield Parish Church"
P (street) 🚻

DRONFIELD (HOLMESDALE) St Philip, Falcon Road

SK 364 792

A 1960's church rebuilt and refurbished to modern standards in 1994. The premises are now in use much of the time during which access to the church should be possible.

SUNDAY SERVICE: 10.00
CHURCH OPEN: when premises are in use
CONTACT: (01246) 413893 (Incumbent)
P (in school CP out of hours)

HEATH All Saints

SK 448 671

The church is by H I Stevens, 1853, and was restored by Butterfield in the 1880's. It replaced an older church lower down the hill. The present building, in Decorated Gothic style with a landmark spire, is at the top NE corner of the village, giving good views over the surrounding countryside. It has a fine collection of Victorian glass. The village itself, with several thatched cottages, is picturesque and quiet, having been by-passed by main roads.

SUNDAY SERVICES: 8.00 (1st), 6.30
FLOWER FESTIVAL: during village well dressing, 3rd week June
CONTACT: (01246) 850339 (Vicar)
Publication: J E Milner, "The Two Churches of Heath"
P (street) 🕯 wc

NORTH WINGFIELD St Lawrence, St Lawrence Road (Grade I)

SK 404 645

The church enjoys a commanding hill site overlooking (northwards) the uppermost reaches of the River Rother; its magnificent C15 tower, 80 feet high, is a well known landmark. The north transept has an elaborately moulded Norman window; apart from this the general body of the church is C15 with a C14 chancel. In the ceiling are C14 tie-beams with carved trefoil tracery. Restoration during the C19 included the rebuilding of the south aisle in 1860. A superb piece of C20 woodwork may be seen in the screen, in the manner of a C15 rood loft with fan-vaulting on the under side; it is by Sir Thomas Jackson (1917) and is worth a visit for this alone.

SUNDAY SERVICES: 8.00 (2nd & 4th only),
10.00, 6.00
CONTACT: (01246) 851181 (Rector) or (01246)
851015 (Mrs Hare)
P 🕯 ♿ wc

St Lawrence, North Wingfield

PILSLEY St Mary the Virgin, Church Street

SK 432 662

Built in 1873 the church has a chancel, nave and large south aisle; there is a bellcote with spirelet. An interesting window design is "The Creation" in the south aisle.

SUNDAY SERVICES: 8.30 (1st & 3rd only), 10.00
CONTACT: (01773) 590529 (Incumbent)
P & wc

WHITTINGTON (or OLD WHITTINGTON) St Bartholomew, Church Street North

SK 384 752

This is a church that presents itself well and has produced helpful printed itineraries for visitors. Its fortunes have been mixed: the mediaeval church was replaced by a new one in 1863. This was fairly conventional, with lean-to aisles and small clerestory windows; its distinguishing feature was the tower at the SW corner surmounted by a high spire. A fire in 1895 left the nave but a shell. The following year, having been rebuilt, the church was re-opened - but this time with larger clerestory windows and, consequently, a higher roof line, reaching up now to the base of the spire (which had survived the fire). There is much stone and wood carving of quality together with interesting stained glass - all fully described in the guide book.

SUNDAY SERVICES: 8.00 (2nd & 4th), 10.30, 6.30 (4.00 in winter)
FLOWER FESTIVAL: June
CONTACT: (01246) 450651 (Rector)
Publications: S W Stones, "The Parish Church of Saint Bartholomew Whittington" also a helpful leaflet, "A Walk around the Parish Church of St Bartholomew's Old Whittington"
P (street) & wc

DERBY CITY

ALLENTON St Edmund, Sinfin Avenue

SK 371 319

A most attractive stone Gothic church built in 1939. Across the road is the 1949 Derby War Memorial Village - 30 houses in a pleasant, open setting with special features for the needs of its disabled occupants. The church itself is light and airy with excellent musical acoustics. In the Lady Chapel is a crucifix by Ronald Pope and a wood carving of Our Lady.

SUNDAY SERVICES: 8.00, 10.00, 6.00
CONTACT: (01332) 701194 (Vicar)
[P] [WC]

ALLESTREE Methodist, Duffield Road

SK 351 399

A plain, red brick chapel in Gothic style, built in 1894. A prized possession is the early 19th century chamber organ which is understood to have come from a chapel in Duffield.

SUNDAY SERVICE: 10.45
CHURCH OPEN (coffee): Sat 10.00-12.00 (Easter to September)
[P] (street)

ALLESTREE St John's Methodist, Birchover Way

SK 341 387

A 1950's building adjacent to Park Farm, the main shopping precinct of a large, post-war housing estate.

SUNDAY SERVICES: 10.30, 6.30
PREMISES OPEN (luncheon club): Wed & Thur
[P] [▣] (above times) [WC]

ALLESTREE St Nicholas, Allestree Lane

SK 341 397

Built in 1958 of brick with stone dressings and in the simplified Gothic style favoured in the immediate after-war years. Like others of its genre it needs to be entered to be appreciated. The interior is spacious and well-proportioned, the bare surfaces and vaults providing the sort of acoustics that are so encouraging for the music of worship (a quality that is understood and made good use of here).

SUNDAY SERVICES: 10.00, 6.30
CONTACT: (01332) 550224 (Vicar)
P & wc

ALVASTON St Michael & All Angels, Church Street

SK 393 333

The church was entirely rebuilt by H I Stevens of Derby in 1855-56, the only trace of anything older being, seemingly, a Saxon coffin lid and some C18 ironwork by Robert Bakewell from a former reredos (containing a figure of St Michael).

SUNDAY SERVICES: 8.30, 10.30
CONTACT: (01332) 571143 (Vicar)
P ⚱ wc

BOULTON St Mary the Virgin, Boulton Lane (Alvaston)

SK 385 331

St Mary's is witness to a very interesting process of growth. Evidence of a small mediaeval building is to be seen in the two Norman doors, a C14 porch and some Perpendicular windows. Enlargements took place in 1840 and 1870. Finally, in c1960, Sebastian Comper supervised a further overall enlargement resulting in a church of quite major proportions. Comper's scheme provided a very elegant Classical stone organ balcony at the west end. However - no doubt on account of the great length of the church - the present organ has been brought two bays forward of this balcony and very daringly suspended over the nave seating area. The East window is a representation of the Passion by Walker J Pearce (1913).

SUNDAY SERVICES: 8.00, 10.15, 5.00 (+ 7.30 on 2nd & 4th)
CHURCH OPEN: daily, 9.30-10-30
CONTACT: (01332) 571296 (Incumbent)
P (Barrett Street) 🗋 ⓘ 💻 ♿ WC

CHADDESDEN St Mary, Church Lane (Grade A)

SK 382 369

This must be one of the best, though one of the least known, parish churches within the present-day City boundary - as is betokened by its prestigious "A" listing. Much of the church dates from its rebuilding during the 1350's as a college or chantry foundation. As at Sandiacre, Norbury and elsewhere, its chief glory lies in the large chancel which is entered through a C15 carved rood screen with east-facing misericord seats on its inner side. Also within the chancel are a stone Gospel desk, sedilia and piscina, all of the C14. The fine triptych behind the high altar is by Walter Tapper (1904).

SUNDAY SERVICES: 8.00, 10.00, 6.30
CHURCH OPEN: Sat & Sun 2.00-4.00 (May to September)
Publication: "Welcome to the Historic Parish Church of St Mary Chaddesden, Derby" - an exemplary guide leaflet, interestingly presented
P 🗋 ⓘ ♿ WC

CHELLASTON St Peter, Chellaston High Street

SK 381 304

The nave and south aisle date essentially from the C13 with the chancel from the following century. The tower was rebuilt in 1842 and much further rebuilding and restoration took place in the 1880's. The pipes of a modern organ are situated over the tower arch at the west end. The church is small for what is now a large suburb and there is talk of expanding the building.

SUNDAY SERVICES: 8.00, 10.00, 6.00
FLOWER FESTIVAL: last w/e June
CONTACT: (01332) 704835 (Vicar)
P ♿

DARLEY ABBEY St Matthew, Church Lane

SK 351 388

The village grew at first around the mediaeval Augustinian Abbey of St Mary. From the late C18 the site was to become an important industrial cotton community. The well-preserved village is now a conservation area. The prettily "Gothick" church was consecrated in 1819, its benefactor being Walter Evans, son of the creator of the mill and its associated community. The sanctuary would at that time have been no more than a recess projecting from the otherwise rectangular building; the present chancel is a later C19 addition in a more Victorian Gothic style. In the churchyard are several Evans family graves together with those of some victims of the sinking of the "Lusitania". There is also the grave of Alfred Ainger, the hymn writer.

SUNDAY SERVICES: 8.00, 10.00, 6.15
CONTACT: (01332) 553192 (Vicar)
P & wc

DERBY Cathedral of All Saints, Irongate (Grade I)

SK 352 364

The visitor is presented with a wonderful progression: 16th century tower, 18th century nave, 20th century retro-choir. The west tower, 212 feet high and standing right on the street, must be one of the finest creations of late Perpendicular Gothic (1510-1530, by a mason who had worked at King's College, Cambridge). The nave was designed by James Gibbs and completed in 1725. Following elevation (in 1927) to cathedral status the apsed retro-choir extension, designed by Sebastian Comper, was opened in 1972. The tomb of Bess of Hardwick who died in 1607 is an important relic from the mediaeval church. The most striking item of furnishing from the 18th century period is the wrought-iron screen by local iron-smith, Robert Bakewell.

SUNDAY SERVICES: 8.00, 10.45, 6.00
CATHEDRAL OPEN: daily, 8.30-6.00
NEW VISITOR CENTRE: due to open in 2000
CATHEDRAL OFFICE: (01332) 341201
Publications: numerous, including guides in various languages
P (public CP nearby) ⌂ ▯ ⚲ ⚲& wc

Cathedral of All Saints, Derby

DERBY Central United Reformed, Becketwell Lane/ Victoria Street

SK 352 362

The present church was built in 1977 over the top of Debenham's store. The site, however, is a historic one, having been in use for worship since the 17th century. It functions as a city centre community-based church offering a warm welcome to visitors; its rooms are in constant use by various community groups. A Memorial Chapel is available for quiet meditation.

SUNDAY SERVICES: 11.00 & 5.30
ACCESS TO PREMISES: most days (coffee Fri mornings)
CHURCH OFFICE: Mon 5.30-6.30, Tue & Fri 9.30-1200 (01332) 380601 (answerphone) or 346627
P (Colyear St or Abbey St) 📖 ⛪ 💺 (Fri am) ♿ wc

DERBY Queen's Hall Methodist Mission, London Road

SK 359 355

The original 1861 London Road Wesleyan was restructured as a Central Hall in 1927. A suite of connecting rooms was built and the church's galleried interior was refurbished with tip-up seats and a rostrum suitable for concert purposes. In the 1960's the street front was modernized to include a foyer. A serious fire in 1991 destroyed much of the interior including the fine organ. Subsequent rebuilding, however, has resulted in a beautiful example of modern worship design within the framework of an older structure. The church now boasts two excellent organs - a large 2-manual by Hunter (1875) and an early 19th century chamber instrument (which survived the fire) by James Davis.

SUNDAY SERVICES: 10.45 & 6.30
CONTACT: resident Warden on premises or (01332) 348665
P (London Rd or public CP) 📖 wc

DERBY St Alkmund, Kedleston Road

SK 347 372

A striking modern building, opened in 1972 on a new site to replace the former H I Stevens town centre church. The main side wall is of a zig-zag plan, with alternating solidpanels and full length stained glass windows which give a wash of deep, rich colour to the interior. The glass fronted entrance, surmounted by a fibre-glass spire, contains the C14 font and various monuments from the Victorian and earlier churches.

SUNDAY SERVICES: 10.00, 7.00
PARISH OFFICE: (01332) 291236
[P] 🛆 ⛪ 🚹 💷 ♿ [wc]

DERBY St Anne, Whitecross Street/Leaper Street

SK 345 370

The austere red brick exterior - tall nave and chancel, lean-to aisles, no tower - belies an interior that has been very aptly described as "numinous". Consecrated in 1872 it is a building clearly conceived for the highest form of Anglo-Catholic worship - with processional aisles, a spacious sanctuary, a rood carried aloft on a high beam and a windowless east wall totally covered with frescos depicting scenes from the Gospels. Stations, statuary and flickering candles all cry out for plainsong and incense to complete the atmosphere (the former regretfully may not be much in evidence nowadays though the latter is still to be experienced, wafting its way up through the shafts of light from the high clerestory windows). The church also possesses a fine set of Continental vestments, many from C17 and C18.

SUNDAY SERVICES: 8.00, 11.15
CHURCH OPEN: 3rd Sat July & 1st Sat September
CONTACT: (01332) 332681 (Vicar)
[P] 🚹

DERBY St Augustine, Upper Dale Road

SK 350 345

A large, red brick church whose building commenced in 1897. It has a small flèche but no tower. The chancel was the last part to be built, in 1910, with a suite of meeting rooms below. Because of this undercroft structure the chancel floor is exceptionally high (with "the highest altar in the Diocese"); the chancel itself contains good mosaic tiles and panelling.

SUNDAY SERVICES: 10.30, 6.30
ACCESS TO CHURCH: via office, Tue-Fri, 10.00-12.00
CONTACT: (01332) 270837 (Office, at above times) or (01332) 766603 (Rector)
[P] 🛆 🚹 ♿ [wc]

DERBY St John the Evangelist, Bridge Street

SK 346 365

A "Commissioners' Church" dating from 1826-27, it is clearly inspired by King's College Chapel - a long, rectangular Gothic box without any tower but with four tall corner turrets. The interior, with galleries each side, is notable for its use of cast-iron in the window traceries and roof trusses. The apsidal chancel dates from 1872 and the fine "Father" Willis organ was installed in 1875.

SUNDAY SERVICES: 9.45, 6.30
CHURCH OPEN: Sat 10.00-12.00
FLOWER FESTIVAL: last w/e September
CONTACT: (01332) 332681 (Vicar)
P (Street) 🛉 🖻 wc

DERBY St Mark, Francis Street

SK 368 368

A late example of an Arts and Crafts church, dating from 1938 and constructed of hand-made bricks and tiles; the unusual "Deco" interior makes use of pre-stressed concrete and has an effect of vaulted spaciousness.

SUNDAY SERVICE: 9.30
CONTACT: (01332) 340183 (Vicar)
P (street) wc

DERBY St Mary (RC), Bridge Gate (Grade I)

SK 351 368

Built during 1838/39, it is the first important church designed by A W N Pugin and consists of a tall, narrow nave with high aisles and an apsed sanctuary, all in perpendicular Gothic style; the pinnacled tower, containing a large west window, was originally planned to have a slender spire. Later, in 1853, J A Hansom added the very large Lady Chapel in decorated Gothic style, with an altar by Paul Pugin. A major refurbishment of the interior of the whole church was carried out from 1986 to 1989: the effect is now refreshingly beautiful.

SUNDAY MASS: 9.00 11.00 & 6.30
CHURCH OPEN: daily
CHURCH OFFICE: (01332) 346126 (10.00-3.00)
Publication: WJ Lilley, "St. Mary's Church, Derby"
P (adjacent street)   🛈 🛉 (by arrangement)   ♿

DERBY St Mary on the Bridge (Chapel of), St Mary's Bridge (Grade I)

SK 354 367

One of only six surviving bridge chapels in England, this one dates largely from the C14. Below the east wall can be seen the springing of the first arch of the mediaeval bridge (now replaced by an 18th century structure alongside). With support from Lord Lloyd Webber's Open Churches Trust it is now open to the public on a regular basis.

SUNDAY SERVICES: 8.30 & 9.15
CHAPEL OPEN: Tues & Sat 1.00-3.00 mid-Apr to mid-Sept & on Cathedral Tower Open Days
CONTACT: (01332) 341201 (Cathedral office)
P (street)

DERBY St Osmond, London Road (Wilmorton)

SK 373 343

A magnificently lofty, dark red brick Gothic church by P H Currey, built in 1904. Adjacent vicarage and other buildings of the same date, together with a sunken garden containing rare plants and a statue of St Osmond, all contribute to a very pleasing architectural ensemble. The interior contains an interesting Art Nouveau reredos and font. The church is easily accessed from the City Cycle Way (a National Cycle Route).

SUNDAY SERVICES: 10.00, 6.00
CONTACT: (01332) 571329 (Vicar)
GARDEN PARTY: last Sat August
P (at rear, access behind Vicarage)   🛈 🛉 ♿ 🚾

DERBY St Peter, St Peter Street

SK 353 360

The only surviving mediaeval church in the City centre - a town church of the early C14. It has a long chancel whose big Perpendicular east window is particularly impressive. In 1898 the tower was dismantled and rebuilt further west to allow for a lengthening of the nave. Further extensions were constructed at the west end in 1972 to provide a 2-storey suite of parish rooms. Random features in the church interior include a mediaeval Flemish chest and the grave of Percy Willoughby, the first gynaecologist.

SUNDAY SERVICES: 10.45, 6.30
CHURCH OPEN: Sat 10.00-12.00
PARISH OPEN DAY: last Sat June
CONTACT: (01332) 360790
P (public CP)   🚪 ♟ 🚹 🖼 ♿ WC

LITTLEOVER Baptist, Thornhill Road

SK 332 343

The present red brick chapel was built in 1888 for a congregation founded in 1813. The hall to the rear is a later addition. "Traditional worship" with pipe organ is maintained as an important element.

SUNDAY SERVICES: 10.30, 6.30
CONTACT: (01332) 516015 (Mrs Measures)
P WC

LITTLEOVER Methodist, Burton Road

SK 329 344

A modern church dating from 1957 and replacing an earlier, smaller building. Of traditional shape, with large "west" window and dominating pulpit, the interior is characterized by the arrangement of roof beams to represent Praying Hands.

SUNDAY SERVICES: 10.30, 6.15
CONTACT: (01332) 342814 (Minister)

LITTLEOVER St Peter, Church Street

SK 333 342

An example of a former village church, of Norman origin, that has grown during the C19 and C20 in parallel with the suburbanization of its surrounding community. Most notable has been the west end enlargement by Sebastian Comper, 1959-61. An important monument is that of Sir Richard Harpur and his wife, 1635.

SUNDAY SERVICES: 8.00, 10.00, 6.30
CHURCH OPEN: Mon, Wed, Fri 9.30-4.00; Tue, Thur 1.00-4.00
OPEN WEEKEND: Petertide (nearest w/e to 29 June)
CONTACT: (01332) 767802 (Vicar)
P (church hall, Normanton Lane)   🚻

MACKWORTH St Francis, Prince Charles Avenue

SK 321 365

A plain, brick church of the 1950's - an effective enclosure of space and well suited to Anglo-Catholic ritual. The community centre is integral with the church building.

SUNDAY SERVICES: 8.00, 9.30, 6.30 (4.00 in winter)
CHURCH OPEN: daily, 8.00-6.00 (or 4.00 in winter)
CONTACT: (01332) 347690 (Vicar)
P (Thur 10.00-1.00) 🚻

MICKLEOVER All Saints, Etwall Road

SK 305 343

Like Littleover this is another village that has grown out of all recognition and has now been absorbed into Derby suburbia. C14 origins are still clear in the tower and chancel; other remnants of this period include font, piscina, aumbry, stone lectern and various carvings. The main body of the church was rebuilt and enlarged by H I Stevens in the 1850's.

SUNDAY SERVICES: 9.15, 11.15, 6.30
CHURCH OPEN: Sat afternoons (July & August)
FLOWER FESTIVAL: August BH w/e
CONTACT: (01332) 513793 (Vicar)
P 🚻

MICKLEOVER Our Lady of Lourdes (RC), Uttoxeter Road

SK 309 344

Built in 1982 and situated amidst spacious grounds and gardens, it must be the most attractive modern church in the whole county. The building is octagonal in shape with fairly low walls and a high, tent-like roof. The general atmosphere of devotion is enhanced by the rich colours of Robert Hickling's stained glass window, "The Last Supper".

SUNDAY MASS: 8.00, 10.00
CHURCH OPEN: daily
CHURCH OFFICE: (01332) 514107)
[P] [&] [wc]

MICKLEOVER St John, Darwin Road/Devonshire Drive

SK 313 352

A modern church serving the residential area north-east of the old parish church of All Saints. Its history has been unfortunate: a new post-war church to an unconventional design had to be demolished in the 1970's on account of a constructional fault. The present church, plainer and simpler, replaced it.

SUNDAY SERVICES: 8.00, 9.30, 6.30
CHURCH OPEN: 8.00 till dusk
ADVENT FAIR: last Sat November
CONTACT: (01332) 516545 (Vicar)
[P] [D] [♟] [&] [wc]

NORMANTON-BY-DERBY St Giles, Village Street

SK 346 336

An old church, possibly of pre-Norman origin, was demolished in 1861 to make way for the new building designed by F J Robinson, a colleague of Derby's well-known H I Stevens; it was further enlarged in 1903. Items of interest within the church include a Norman tympanum from the old church together with numerous memorials, plaques and other relics of the Sherwood

Foresters based at the former Normanton Barracks and whose regimental garrison church this was.

SUNDAY SERVICES: 8.00, 10.45, 6.30
CHURCH OFFICE: (01332) 776287 (2.30-4.30)
Publication: J Raven, "A Walk Around St Giles' Church"
Ⓟ (street) 🅆🅒

SINFIN St Stephen, Wordsworth Avenue/Sinfin Lane

SK 347 321

A modest brick church of 1935, a late work by local Arts & Crafts architect, P H Currey. The altar, on a platform, is now in the middle of the long north side while a recess - obviously originally designed to be the sanctuary - houses a very attractive 1982 pipe organ by Roger Pulham (Suffolk).

SUNDAY SERVICES: 10.00, 6.30
ACCESS TO CHURCH : via Parish Centre, Mon-Fri 9.00-12.30
REFRESHMENTS: Tue 10.00-12.00 (term time)
CHURCH OFFICE: (01332) 773093 (mornings)
Ⓟ ♿ 🅆🅒

GLOSSOP

CHARLESWORTH Congregational, Monks Road

SK 010 928

An Independent congregation was founded here in 1662 making use of a disused mediaeval chapel. The present building, on the same site, dates from 1797 and stands amidst a large graveyard on an open hillside giving dramatic distant views of Thameside and Greater Manchester. Externally it is much as built, of plain gritstone but with pretty, but slightly incongrous, Venetian windows in the main gabled front. The interior, however, was totally refurbished about a hundred years later. With its continuous gallery round all four sides and much excellent carpentry and ironwork, it represents a perfect late-Victorian chapel interior. In the gallery behind the pulpit stands a large 2-manual Binns organ installed in 1911.

SUNDAY SERVICE: 10.45
CONTACT: (01457) 852738 (Minister) or (01457) 869001 (Deacon)
P (in churchyard) 🚻 ♿ wc

Congregational Chapel, Charlesworth

Chapel Milton, Chinley

CHINLEY Independent (Congregational), Chapel Milton

SK 055 820

Built in 1711 for a congregation founded in 1662, this is second only to Chesterfield Unitarian in age. It is doubtless the jewel in the crown of Derbyshire's dissenting chapels, being the only one to retain its original plan, layout and furnishing. Founded by the ejected Vicar of Glossop, William Bagshawe ("The Apostle of the Peak"), it stands in an old-established churchyard which is an "extra parochial liberty" (ie not within any parish). Built of local stone, it is long and narrow with a gable at each end; windows are single mullioned in the vernacular style of the 17th century. On entering one is transported to the early meeting-house era - 17th century pulpit (from an earlier chapel) in the middle of the long north wall; elegantly panelled and moulded galleries on the three sides facing the pulpit; box pews upstairs and down similarly facing the pulpit; 18th century chandelier fittings; and numerous historic wall monuments. When not open much of the interior may still be seen by looking through the clear glass panes of the lower windows - however, a proper visit is strongly recommended.

SUNDAY SERVICES: 10.30, 6.30
CONTACT: (01663) 750571 (Minister)
Publication: Simpson, "The History of Chinley Chapel, Chinley (Independent), Founded 1662"
P 🛆 ♿ WC

GLOSSOP St Mary Crowned (RC), Sumner Street

SK 030 938

Built in 1882 by the local mill owner, Frances Sumner, the Gothic church is big and lofty. Its cathedral-like acoustics are well matched by the small, though effective 2-manual Gray & Davison organ of 1886.

SUNDAY MASS: 10.00, 6.00
CONTACT: (01457) 853124 (Presbytery)
P (in church grounds)   ⬛ ⬛ ⬛ ⬛ wc

NEW MILLS St George, Church Road/Church Lane

SK 005 854

Of "Commissioners'" type, dating from 1830, with tower and spire, all executed in lancet Gothic style. The chancel was built in 1898 and the original Georgian interior re-ordered in the taste of the time. Remaining from the earlier period, however, are the galleries and the 1835 Samuel Renn organ case (albeit widened and moved to a new location). From Church Road there is a footpath to "The Torrs", the New Mills Heritage and Information Centre (open daily).

SUNDAY SERVICES: 9.30, 6.30
CONTACT: (01663) 747177 (office) or (01663) 743225 (Vicar)
P (street)   ⬛ ⬛ wc

NEW MILLS St James, Spring Bank

SK 001 859

Built in 1880 as a Chapel of Ease for St George's (above). The important feature is its contemporary Victorian interior with original furnishings, painted roof timbers and monochrome murals. There is also a courtyard of almshouses by the same architect linked to the west end of the church. The building is now shared with the local Methodist congregation.

SUNDAY SERVICE: 11.00
CONTACT: (01663) 747177 (St George's office) or (01663) 742331 (Methodist Minister)
P (street)

WHITFIELD St James, Hollincross Lane (Glossop)

SK 032 935

It is difficult to distinguish the boundaries of Whitfield - formerly more important than Glossop and now, though somewhat overshadowed by the latter, still managing to preserve an attractive identity within the larger conurbation. The church, dating from 1846, stands out on account of its fine broach spire. Some stained glass in the south aisle is to a design by Burne-Jones. The very large pipe organ was rebuilt in 1937, and the story goes that the organ builders' lorry suffered an accident coming over the Woodhead Pass; this was said to have caused the wind to moan through the "disconsolate pipes as they lay in the bleak fields"!

SUNDAY SERVICES: 11.00 (weekly), 6.30 (1st, 2nd, 3rd & 5th)
CONTACT: (01457) 861948 (Mrs Davenport)
P (street) ♀ ♿ wc

WHITFIELD St Luke, Fauvel Road (Glossop)

SK 033 943

Though a substantial late Victorian Gothic building, this is in fact still a chapel of ease serving the northern portion of the parish of St James (see above). Its finest possession is the 3-manual tracker action organ installed by Conacher in 1906 - amongst the dozen or so most important instruments in the County and still unspoilt by modern "improvers". The organ probably does not feature, though, in the annual "Jazz Service" at 10.30 on the first Sunday of July.

SUNDAY SERVICES: 9.45 (weekly), 6.30 (4th only)
CONTACT: (01457) 864195 (Mrs Booth)
P (street) ♀ wc

HEANOR & RIPLEY

ALDERCAR St John, Cromford Road

SK 445 479

An attractive, small chapel of ease within the parish of Langley Mill. It dates from 1871 and the main architectural feature is an apse with glass by W Ramsay. The west window displays symbols of the four evangelists.

SUNDAY SERVICE: 9.30
CONTACT: (01773) 712441 (Vicar)
P (street)   &   wc

CODNOR St James, Crosshills/Denby Lane

SK 418 487

A small "Commissioners'" church, built in 1844 in the lancet style and with a west gallery on cast-iron columns. The chancel dates from 1890. The font, found in 1834 in the precincts of Codnor Castle, is now in a small chapel dedicated to St Nicholas (as was the old castle chapel).

SUNDAY SERVICES: 8.00, 10.00, 6.30
CONTACT: (01773) 742516 (Vicar)
Publication: F S Thorpe, "A History of St James Church Codnor"
P (street)   🗋   &   wc

DENBY St Mary the Virgin, Church Street (Grade I)

SK 399 464

Entering from the south east along the churchyard path the view is entirely mediaeval and orthodox: C14 chancel and tower (with spire), nave with C15 clerestory. Inside, however, the effect is curiously lopsided. The late Norman south arcade of two bays is still in place (the oldest surviving part of the church), but the north arcade was removed in 1838 and its aisle raised to the height of the nave roof in order to accommodate a gallery - which still remains, accommodating at its east end the splendid 1914 Harrison & Harrison organ. An upper row of C15 style clerestory windows give the north exterior elevation an unusual two-storeyed appearance. A C17 memorial in the chancel is to Patrick Lowe of Locko Park, his wife and children.

SUNDAY SERVICE: 10.00
CONTACT: (01332) 780730 (Incumbent)
FLOWER FESTIVAL: 2nd Sun September
P (opposite)

HEANOR St Lawrence, Market Place

SK 435 465

This is the fourth church on the site, the previous one having been little more than a century old (save for its fine C15 tower) when subsidence started to cause problems. The years 1981-82 therefore saw yet another new start, retaining the mediaeval tower, the north nave arcade and some lower aisle walling. The result, by Kenneth Murta, is an interesting modern design enhanced by old fragments (including Victorian glass), providing a flexible space for worship together with good social and other facilities.

SUNDAY SERVICES: 10.00, 6.30 (4.30 in winter)
CHURCH OPEN: daily (ex Sun), 9.00-5.00
CONTACT: (01773) 765803 or (01773) 762350 (Churchwardens) or (01773) 719800 (Vicar)
P (public CP)   &   WC

HORSLEY WOODHOUSE St Susanna, Main Street/ Church Lane

SK 396 449

A small church dating from 1881. Contains some C19 stained glass; there is also an interesting late C19 organ case that may have come from a private house.

SUNDAY SERVICE: 6.30
CONTACT: (01332) 883443 (Mr Slater)
SUMMER CELEBRATION: 1st Sun July
P (by Church Hall)   WC

LANGLEY MILL St Andrew, Station Road

SK 446 470

A magnificent stone church by J S Brocklesby, built 1911-13. It is one of the highlights of the Arts and Crafts movement - the style being basically a rugged early Gothic (Iona Abbey comes to mind by way of comparison) with hints of Romanesque. There is a massive central tower whose internal ceiling is stone vaulted. The building's outstanding quality may sometimes be a little lost by virtue of its semi-industrial surroundings; however, it is well used, having become in recent years the centre of a lively Anglican/Methodist ecumenical partnership.

SUNDAY SERVICES: 10.30, 6.00
CHURCH OPEN: Mon 12.30-2.00
CONTACT: (01773) 712441 (Vicar)
P (street)   &   WC

MORLEY St Matthew, Church Lane (Grade I)

SK 396 409

Beautifully situated, adjacent to the old Rectory (now a Diocesan Retreat House), and full of wonderful treasures. The architecture itself is fine, ranging from Norman to 15th century, but it is its contents that most visitors will relish, particularly the 14th century stained glass from Dale Abbey (now in the NE chapel) and the numerous monuments of the Sacheverell family dating from 15th to 18th centuries. Also from Dale Abbey are the mediaeval floor tiles and the south porch. In the tower arch is the small organ by Hill (1885) with its elegant Gothic case (1899) inspired by that of the 14th century instrument at Sion, Switzerland (the oldest existing organ).

CHURCH SERVICE: 11.00
CHURCH OPEN: Sat 2.00-4.00 (Easter till Harvest)
Publication: G Compton-Bracebridge, "A History of St Matthew's Church Morley"
(with pen & ink   illustrations by its author)
CONTACT: (01332) 880380 (Incumbent)
P   ▯   ♟   ♦   &   WC

RIPLEY All Saints

SK 399 506

Ripley is a bustling market town, clearly visible from many directions on its hilltop site, the two highest features being the Town Hall (former Market Hall) and All Saints' tower. The church itself is of Commissioners' Gothic and dates from 1821. It is set back from the road, hemmed in by buildings to the west but with an attractive churchyard approach on the south side. The interior is open and aisleless with a wide west gallery; it is comfortable and has all modern facilities.

St Andrew, Langley Mill

SUNDAY SERVICES: 9.15, 11.00, 6.30 (10.00 & 6.30 only on 1st)
CHURCH OPEN: Sat mornings + most weekday mornings
🅿 (Moseley Street, behind church hall)

SMALLEY St John the Baptist, Main Road

SK 407 446

The present church was first constructed (on an ancient site) in 1793. Subsequent additions and alterations, however, have removed any traces of the C18 work. Its most unusual feature is the almost (but not quite) detached Arts & Crafts belfry with a pretty, pyramid roof, added to house the chime of five bells donated by a former Incumbent. This chime, by Taylor of Loughborough, with the Tenor weighing over 2 tons, is said to be the heaviest in England.

SUNDAY SERVICES: 9.30, 6.30
CONTACT: (01332) 880380 (Incumbent) 🅿 (street)   ♿ ｗｃ

ILKESTON & LONG EATON

BREASTON St Michael (Grade I)

SK 460 335

St Michael's began in the early C13 as a chapel within Sawley parish; expansion into the south aisle was probably later in the same century, leaving the church much as it still is. The most notable feature is the very tiny Gothic chancel arch - an obvious handicap since it reduces the choir almost to a separate room, much in the "cellular" manner of many Saxon churches. There is an elegant Derbyshire alabaster font of 1720 and a small modern organ by Church & Co (1975).

SUNDAY SERVICES: 8.00, 9.30, 6.30
CHURCH OPEN: Thur 2.30-4.30 & Sat 10.30-12.00
CONTACT: (01332) 872112 or (01332) 872753 (Churchwardens)   P   ⛎

DALE ABBEY All Saints (Grade I)

SK 435 381

Of the pre-Reformation abbey church of St Mary nought remains but the arch of the great east window and a few ground level fragments. Some of its furnishings have now found their way to new resting places: stained glass to Morley Church, font cover and benches to Radbourne Church, while the C15 font is in the present All Saints' Church. The latter, joined to a domestic building, was in fact a chapel on the perimeter of the Abbey precinct. It is tiny - no more than about 25 feet square - of Norman origin though with mostly Perpendicular architectural details. Its chief glory, however, is the unspoilt ensemble of early C17 interior furnishings, crammed together (as they always have been) in the most curious manner. Only 200 yards from the church is a hermit's cave which preceded the foundation of the Abbey.

SUNDAY SERVICE: 3.00
CHURCH OPEN: Sat, Sun & BH, 2.00-5.00
OPEN FOR WELL DRESSING: May Day BH
KEY AVAILABLE: from Manor House, Dale Abbey village (0115) 932 0593
Publication: R Allen & I Gooding, "The Abbey at Dale" - a very well produced booklet with excellent colour photographs
P (in village, not at church)   B   (Other facilities at Gateway Centre in village - see below)

72

DALE ABBEY Gateway Christian Centre

SK 436 387

This is housed in the village's former Methodist (Wesleyan) Chapel of 1902. It is available for retreats and conferences and also contains a shop for refreshments, cards, craft items, etc. As the above-mentioned booklet states: "You can be sure of a warm Christian welcome when you visit Dale".

CENTRE OPEN: daily

P 🗋 👤 🛈 WC

All Saints, Dale Abbey

DRAYCOTT St Mary

SK 445 332

Though strictly only a mission church, St Mary's actually serves the main population of the village, the old parish church being at Wilne, a mile away and in total isolation. The building is in fact a former Wesleyan chapel of 1832, in fairly standard late Georgian style with galleries at sides and back. An incongruously Gothic "chancel" was added during the Methodist era. The building came into Anglican use in 1966.

SUNDAY SERVICES: 11.00, 6.30 (October till Easter, otherwise at Wilne)
OPEN FOR COFFEE: 1st Sat 10.00 (in Hall)
CONTACT: (01332) 874974 or (01332) 872893 (Churchwardens)
P (street)

ILKESTON Holy Trinity, Granby Street

SK 464 427

A large, towerless Victorian town church built in 1884 in Early English style. In view of its great size and the high quality of its architecture and fittings it is most surprising to find that it has no mention in Pevsner's coverage. In recent years the nave has been partitioned to form a church hall in the western half, while below the Rood beam the congregational chairs now spread up the steps into a part of the former chancel. Happily one can still appreciate the great loftiness of the whole concept, compensating in some measure for the curtailment of the horizontal vista. Fittings, furnishings and vestments are all contemporary and of the highest order, in keeping with a major church designed for Anglo Catholic ritual. Special mention must also be made of the magnificent 1909 Harrison & Harrison organ.

SUNDAY SERVICES: 9.00, 10.30, 6.00
CHURCH OPEN: daily, 8.00-11.00
CONTACT: (0115) 932 0833 (Vicar)
P (street)

ILKESTON St John the Evangelist, Nottingham Road

SK 472 408

A large, tall red brick church by Arts and Crafts architect, P H Currey (1912). It has long, slender lancet windows, no tower but a turret between nave and north transept. The chancel is particularly impressive, with the fine Keates organ (1919) perched loftily over the stalls in a cathedral-like position. The Lady Chapel is kept as a quiet area for prayer.

SUNDAY SERVICES: 8.00, 10.00, 6.00
CHURCH OPEN: Wed, 9.30-12.30
CONTACT: (0115) 932 5446 (Vicar)
P

KIRK HALLAM All Saints, Ladywood Road (Ilkeston) (Grade I)

SK 458 405

A small, aisleless church, mostly of C14 and C15, though with surviving Norman fragnents in the form of two beakheads (preserved in the porch) and a tub-shaped font.

SUNDAY SERVICES: 9.30, 6.00
CONTACT: (0115) 932 2402 (Priest-in-Charge)
P

LONG EATON St Laurence, Market Place

SK 492 338

G E Street, in 1868, carried out a very successful enlargement in which the old nave and chancel (Norman, rebuilt C14) were retained as the south aisle of his new building. A happy result of this arrangement is that the C15 tower (and spire) is now in a SW location, allowing the nave to display a facade containing a large west window.

SUNDAY SERVICES: 8.00, 10.00, 6.00
CHURCH OPEN: daily, at various unspecified times
CONTACT: (0115) 973 3154 (Vicar)
P (Waverley Street, at east end of church)   &   wc

MAPPERLEY Holy Trinity

SK 434429

A former mining village on the edge of Shipley Country Park. The first church (1851) had to be dismantled following mining subsidence; the present one dates from 1966. It is a modern building with much use of glass though a number of older features have been incorporated, such as stained glass, some pit memorial tablets and the war memorial lychgates. Trees in the churchyard were planted by a local school for Arbor Day.

SUNDAY SERVICE: 9.30
CONTACT: (0115) 932 4706 (Churchwarden)
P (street)   wc

OCKBROOK Moravian Church & Settlement

SK 421 362

The church cannot be considered without the Settlement of which it forms the nucleus: it must be seen as a whole. The Moravians, a pre-Reformation Protestant body established in Bohemia in the 15th century, arrived in Ockbrook in 1740 and the regular congregation was founded in 1750, followed shortly by various houses, workshops and then by the School in 1799. The whole Settlement is now designated a Conservation Area. The church itself dates from 1752 and may best be described as being in an attractive, red-brick New England Georgian style with a pretty, white cupola over the main gable facade. The interior retains its original gallery and plastered ceiling though the general layout was re-ordered during the 19th century.

SUNDAY SERVICES: 11.00, 6.30 (3.15 on 1st Sun instead of 6.30)
CONTACT: (01332) 662319 (Minister)
GUIDED TOURS OF THE SETTLEMENT: may be arranged for parties in summer time by arrangement with the Minister; tours will include a display of archive material and needlework from the Sisters' House (+ refreshments)
Publication: A McGibbon & H Todd, "Ockbrook Moravian Church and Settlement"

RISLEY All Saints, Derby Road

SK 461 357

The conservation area sits astride the old A52 road and consists of Risley Hall (part C17), the various School buildings (early C18) together with All Saints' Church, built in 1593 and one of very few in the whole country dating from Elizabeth's reign. As built the church had a small tower and a nave with no chancel or sanctuary division. The north aisle, which projects westwards to contain the organ, was added in 1841.

SUNDAY SERVICE: 9.30
CONTACT: (0115) 949 1669 (Mr Lane) or (0115) 939 5715 (Dr Lester)
Ⓟ (street) Ⓗ ⌷wc⌷

SANDIACRE St Giles, Church Drive (Grade I)

SK 480 372

The present-day community of Sandiacre has grown up in an area to the south of the church, leaving the latter still in a situation of apparently rural seclusion. The church, on a high eminence, represents three important building phases - 12th century nave, 13th century spire and 14th century chancel. Inside there could not be a greater contrast than there is between the simple, aisleless Norman nave and the magnificent Decorated chancel with its great windows and original sedilia. Linking these two sections is a finely carved Norman chancel arch, some distance above which is a small triangular-headed opening - a remnant of the earlier Saxon building. At the west end, within a double case and on a purpose-built gallery, is a fine 2-manual organ by Church & Co. (1977).

SUNDAY SERVICES: 8.00, 9.30 (+ 6.30 on 1st)
KEY AVAILABLE: from Rectory, opposite church gate
P   🗋

STANLEY St Andrew, Station Road

SK 416 404

The area was once busy with the coal mining industry but has now mainly reverted to quiet rurality. Stanley, being on the edge of this area, escaped the worst excesses and still remains a country village. The church has Norman and C13 remnants but was largely rebuilt in 1875. It has a Jacobean pulpit and altar rails and there is a rare version of the royal arms of William III. In the churchyard look out for the epitaph to Luke Woodward, the village blacksmith.

SUNDAY SERVICE: 11.15
CONTACT: (0115) 932 8276 (Mr Walters)
P (street)

STANTON-BY-DALE St Michael & All Angels, Stanhope Street

SK 464 381

A peaceful village on a hill overlooking the vast Stanton Ironworks complex. The nucleus of the village, now a conservation area, was developed and owned until 1912 by the Earl of Stanhope. The church is mostly of about 1300. Three windows by Kempe show scenes of the ironworks and pipe-making; in the churchyard is a memorial to a war-time bomber crew killed in the parish.

SUNDAY SERVICES: 10.45, 6.30
CONTACT: (0115) 932 4843 or (0115) 932 9706
P (street)

WEST HALLAM St Wilfrid

SK 432 411

The tower is C15; the body of the church is mostly C14 with considerable rebuilding in 1855. There are some Tudor monuments to the Powtrell family though the fine Elizabethan communion rail noted by Pevsner seems to have gone.

SUNDAY SERVICES: 11.00, 5.00, 6.30
CONTACT: (0115) 932 4695 (Rector)
OPEN FOR WELL DRESSING: 2nd w/e July
Ⓟ (street) ♿ 🚻

WILNE (or CHURCH WILNE) St Chad, Wilne Road (Grade I)

SK 448 318

The church occupies a remote and lonely spot on the Derwent flood plain, a mile short of where this river flows into the Trent. The spacious church originally served a very large area, which included Draycott, Breaston and Risley, but the population gradually moved away from Wilne, a site that was prone to flooding. The main body of the church dates from C14 and C15. Then in 1624 came a substantial addition when the south aisle was extended to form the Willoughby family chapel with its contemporary stained glass (probably Flemish, by Van Linges) and its collection of family monuments. A bad fire in 1917 destroyed most of the interior fittings though the Willoughby Chapel survived more or less unscathed. Restoration, with new furnishings in Arts and Crafts style, was carried out under P H Currey. It is refreshing not to find evidence of Victorian "restoration" (always, in reality, something of a contradiction in terms); the work by Currey, in spite of (or perhaps because of) its originality, seems to engender much more of a mediaeval atmosphere than does the well-meaning work of many of the Victorian architects. A walk around the nearby lake may also be recommended.

SUNDAY SERVICES: 11.00 (1st only), 6.30 (Easter till Harvest)
FLOWER FESTIVAL: Summer BH w/e
CONTACT: (01332) 874974 or (01332) 872893 (Churchwardens)
Ⓟ 🕯

LONGFORD & SUDBURY

BOYLESTONE St John the Baptist

SK 183 357

The church is mostly of the C14. On the inner north wall of the chancel is a finely moulded recess of this period. Also in the chancel, below the C15 east window, is a carved reredos of the Last Supper. The SW tower, with pyramidal roof and concave sides, dates from 1844.

SUNDAY SERVICE: 9.30 (3rd & 4th), 6.45 (1st & 2nd : 3.00 in winter)
CONTACT: (01335) 330550 (Mr Pelly) or (01283) 585296 (Rector)
🅿 (Village Hall CP)

CHURCH BROUGHTON St Michael, Church Street (Grade I)

SK 205 337

Visibly the church is mostly of the C14 though its Norman origins are apparent in a scalloped capital in the north aisle and the finely carved font. There are connections with the family of W H Auden, whose uncle and cousin were both Vicars of the parish; the poet himself is known to have spent some holidays here.

SUNDAY SERVICES: 8.00 & 10.00 (1st), 9.30 (2nd, 3rd & 4th)
CONTACT: (01283) 585350 (Mr & Mrs Crawford)
OPEN FOR VILLAGE MAY FESTIVAL: May Day BH
🅿 (street) 📖

DALBURY All Saints, The Lane

SK 264 344

A remote little church, architecturally plain but nevertheless full of interest. Basically it is a simple chapel, probably of the C13, but enlarged (north aisle) under the incumbency of The Revd Charles Cotton, Rector from 1831 to 1857. Mr Cotton was a skilled wood carver and much of the woodwork in the church is clearly by him, including probably the old organ casework now at the west end. The present functioning organ (in the chancel) is an early C19 chamber instrument by Flight & Robson. A recently acquired treasure is the c1200 stained glass figure of St Michael - probably the oldest glass in

Derbyshire. The church is located on the footpath known as "Three Churches Walk" (Dalbury-Trusley-Sutton).

SUNDAY SERVICE: 11.00 (3rd only), 3.00 (1st only)
CHURCH OPEN: daily
P (in lane)

DOVERIDGE St Cuthbert, Church Lane (Grade I)

SK 114 341

The church is right on the western edge of the village, overlooking the Dove and across into Staffordshire. The approach through the churchyard is under a "tunnel" formed by the branches of an ancient yew, said to be over 1,000 years old. The most important feature of the church is its fine, long, early C13 chancel still with its original lancet windows; it is of the same proportions as the nave and there is no dividing arch between the two. The aisles were added in the C14. The C20 has seen the addition of an octagonal meeting room which is entered via the north porch.

SUNDAY SERVICES: 8.00, 10.45
CONTACT: (01889) 562556 or (01889) 502457 (Churchwardens)
P (street)

EGGINTON St Wilfrid (Grade I)

SK 268 279

The church, on a Norman site, dates mainly from the early 1300's, with only the tower of the later Perpendicular period. Some early C14 glass still remains in the east window. Various memorials and hatchments are to be seen of the local Every and Moseley families. On display in a glass case are a flute and clarinet used by the early C19 church band. Outside, on the south wall of the chancel, there is a mediaeval scratch dial.

SUNDAY SERVICES: 9.30, 3.00
KEY AVAILABLE: from St Wilfrid's House, next to church gates, 9.00-12.00, 2.30-4.00
CONTACT: (01283) 733025 (Churchwarden) or (01283) 732349 (Incumbent)
Publication: J B Henderson, "The Story of Egginton and its Church St Wilfrid's"
P ⌂ ♿ wc

ETWALL St Helen (Grade I)

SK 269 320

This church has a lot to offer the visitor. It is well set off, the churchyard being raised above the level of the nearby main road. To the north are the C16 John Port almshouses (known as Etwall Hospital) with their C18 Robert Bakewell wrought iron gates leading to the churchyard. The external appearance of the church is late Perpendicular, the large windows on the south side of the nave probably being Gothic survival of the C17 or even C18. Inside, however, we encounter a fine C12 Norman north arcade, while the north chancel wall has a C13 built-in stone lectern (or Gospel Shelf). Also in the chancel is the canopied tomb (1541) of Sir John Port (not only the founder of the Hospital but also of Repton School). Perhaps the most fascinating feature is the Port Chapel at the east end of the north aisle. It now contains the superb ensemble of carved pews and desk (1635) which until 1816 were at the west end of the north aisle and were used for daily prayers by the Master of the Hospital and almsmen.

SUNDAY SERVICES: 11.00, 6.30
CHURCH OPEN: 1st Sat 1.00-4.00
(April - October); also 2nd Sat
September all day
OPEN FOR WELL DRESSING:
3rd Sat May
CONTACT: (01283) 732349
(Incumbent) or (01283)
733344 (Churchwarden)
Publication:
B Henderson. "Know
Your Parish Church St
Helen's, Etwall"

P 🕯 👤 ♿ WC

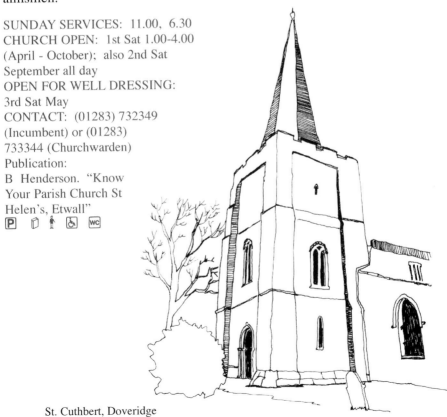

St. Cuthbert, Doveridge

LONGFORD St Chad, Longford Hall Park (Grade I)

SK 215 383

The church is light and spacious - a quality due in considerable part to the height of the nave and the general absence of stained glass. Some arcading and pillars survive from the Norman church, but most of what you see is C14 and C15. The Longford family were Lords of the Manor until C16 and their numerous monuments, cleaned and conserved in 1984, have now been moved from the south to the north aisle. The family were succeeded as owners of the estate by the Cokes whose most celebrated member was the agriculturist, Thomas William Coke, 1st Earl of Leicester ("Coke of Holkham"), to whom there is a marble bust within a decorated Gothic canopy (1842). The organ, with its curiously oriental looking casework, is a particularly fine instrument by Isaac Abbott (1874) in the style of the German organ builder, Edmund Schulze. Longford Hall (to the south of the churchyard) is not normally accessible to the public though the gardens are usually open on one Sunday in July.

SUNDAY SERVICE: 9.30 (4th), 10.00 (3rd), 11.00 (1st), 6.30 (2nd)
CHURCH OPEN: weekends (summer)
CONTACT: (01335) 330446 (Mr Lenderyou) or (01335) 330472 (Mr Hill) or (01283) 585296 (Rector)
P (in old stable yard north of church)

LONG LANE Christ Church

SK 253 380

An attractive brick Gothic church of 1859 - quite simple, with aisleless nave and chancel. A saddleback tower and vestry were added in 1874 on the north side of the chancel.

SUNDAY SERVICE: 8.30 (2nd), 11.00 (4th), 7.00 (1st & 3rd)
CONTACT: (01335) 824414 (Mr Jackson) or (01283) 585296 (Rector)
P (street)

MARSTON MONTGOMERY St Giles

SK 135 379

The village takes its name from the Montgomery family who owned land in this neighbourhood. Its small church has a Norman nave and chancel while the north aisle was added in the early C13. There is no tower, but the west gable of the nave is surmounted by a very pretty, pyramidal bellcote (by St Aubyn) dating from 1877. The small Conacher organ was installed in 1885; a wall plaque tells us that Evelyn Wood played this instrument for seventy years and died in 1997 at the age of 101.

SUNDAY SERVICE: 8.30 (1st), 11.00 (2nd & 4th), 5.45 (3rd), united on 5th (in rotation)
CONTACT: (01335) 324516 (Mrs Whitfield)
OPEN FOR WELL DRESSING: 2nd Sun June
P (village hall)

MARSTON-ON-DOVE St Mary, Marston Lane (Grade I)

SK 233 296

This church possesses many curiosities, architectural and otherwise, and well deserves its Grade I listing. It stands within a large, exposed churchyard in a remote part of the Dove flood-plain. At one time it stood adjacent to a loop of the river, but this was cut off by the construction of the railway to the south of the church. The most striking thing is the large nave roof rising from a 2-storeyed north wall, the upper windows of which date (according to Pevsner) from a C15 alteration in which the north aisle must have been incorporated into a wider nave (or was it, as at Denby, an enlargement in the early C19 to accommodate a north gallery?). Once inside the openness and lightness of the nave is very striking as is also the exceptionally wide C13 chancel. The C14 south aisle, with its elegant arcade, is of more orthodox proportions. Two

St Wilfrid, Egginton

highly valued possessions are the oldest bell in Derbyshire (1366) and the earliest surviving organ case in the county (late C17/early C18, originally in Sudbury Hall).

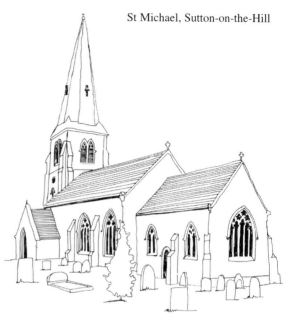

St Michael, Sutton-on-the-Hill

SUNDAY SERVICE: 11.00
(+ 9.30 on 2nd & 5th)
CONTACT: (01283) 733433
(Vicar)
P ⚲ ♿ wc

RADBOURNE St Andrew, Church Lane (Grade I)

SK 286 360

The church stands in the grounds of Radbourne Hall (which is not visitable, though there is a pleasant footpath across the Park with some good views). Most of the present building is of C14 and C15 - consisting of chancel and nave plus a north aisle at the west end of which is the tower. Late mediaeval carved benches came from Dale Abbey (near Ilkeston) following the Dissolution. There are several C15 monuments to members of the de la Pole family whose descendants still live in the Hall, together with a large Baroque wall-monument by Grinling Gibbons (1683) to German Pole. The carved Gothic organ case in the chancel houses an instrument by Conacher (1889).

SUNDAY SERVICE: 9.30 (4th - winter only), 11.00 (2nd), 6.30 (4th - summer only)
CHURCH OPEN: weekends (summer)
CONTACT: (01332) 824237 (Mrs Smith) or (01283) 585296 (Rector)
P (street - limited)

SCROPTON St Paul, Scropton Road

SK 193 302

This Victorian church dates from 1856, replacing an earlier one; its most distinguishing external feature is the pyramid roof of the west tower. Of particular interest internally are the twelve copper panels set in the altar and reredos with C18 paintings showing statues of the Apostles in their niches (inspired by those in St John Lateran, Rome); the c1510 incised tomb slab of Nicholas Agard and his two wives is also worth noting.

SUNDAY SERVICE: 9.30 (1st & 3rd), 6.30 (2nd, 4th & 5th)
CONTACT: (01283) 812963 or (01283) 585383 (Churchwardens)
ℙ (street)

SOMERSAL HERBERT St Peter

SK 136 352

Though of earlier origin and with an unusual former dedication to St Blaise, the present church dates from 1874, the tower being added in 1912. Survivors from the earlier building include the 18th century brick porch with its attractive rusticated stone quoins, together with a Norman font decorated with characteristic intersecting arches.

SUNDAY SERVICE: 10.00
KEY AVAILABLE: from Church Cottage, opposite
CONTACT: (01283) 585593 or (01288) 585358 (Churchwardens)
ℙ (on road)

SUDBURY All Saints

SK 157 321

In spite of a rather heavy restoration during 1874-5 there is much of interest in this church - not least its superb location adjacent to the 17th century Sudbury Hall (NT property), through whose grounds there is public access to the churchyard. The glass in the east window was given by Queen Victoria and Prince Albert in 1850. There are numerous monuments to the Vernon family from the Hall next door, the earliest being c1300, the rest dating from the 17th century to the 19th. Also worthy of note is the fine 3-manual Nicholson & Lord organ, built c1875 but including pipes from an earlier instrument.

SUNDAY SERVICE: 11.15 (10.00 on 4th)
CHURCH OPEN: daily
ℙ (NT car park available) 𝕯

SUTTON-ON-THE-HILL St Michael, Church Road
SK 237 342

Of the C14 church the tower (with its tall 1841 spire), north aisle arcade and part of the chancel remain. The general impression, however, is of the 1863 rebuilding - and very impressive it is too on its prominent rural hill site. When the C17 monument on the north wall of the chancel was dismantled for conservation a bricked up C14 window was discovered containing armorial glass of c1330. A statue of St Michael came from the redundant Derby church of the same name. The church is linked to Dalbury and Trusley by "The Three Churches Walk".

SUNDAY SERVICE: 11.00
CONTACT: (01283) 733433 (Mrs
Martindale) or (01283) 732603 (Mrs
Shirley) or (01283) 585296 (Rector)
P (street) ♿

TRUSLEY All Saints
SK 254 355

The working village of Trusley, centred on its church, was designated a Conservation Area in 1968 - one of the earliest in Derbyshire. The church, replacing an earlier one, is a small, aisleless, red brick building of 1713 in the style of Wren. Features include a fine Baroque south porch (which, it is suggested, may have come from elsewhere) and an interior still retaining its original box pews, three-decker pulpit, font and other furnishings -

Doorway or All Saints, Trusley

including the largest collection of funeral hatchments in the county. The church also possesses a "Maiden's Garland" (or virgin's funeral crown). It is connected to Sutton-on-the-Hill and Dalbury by "The Three Churches Walk".

SUNDAY SERVICE: 11.00 (1st, 2nd, 3rd & 5th), 6.45 (4th)
CHURCH OPEN: weekends (summer)
CONTACT: (01283) 732760) (Mr Goodall) or (01283) 585296 (Rector)
Publication: D Buckley, "The Parish Church of All Saints, Trusley"
P (street) ♿

MATLOCK & WIRKSWORTH

ALDERWASLEY All Saints

SK 325 532

All Saints was built in 1850 by Francis Edward Hurt of Alderwasley Hall in whose grounds it stands. Until 1931 it was a private chapel but, on sale of the house, it became a chapel-of-ease within Wirksworth parish. The fine Brindley & Foster organ in the north transept was given by Mr A F Hurt in 1880. Not far away is the C15 chapel of St Margaret, replaced by All Saints and left derelict for many years; it has now been restored as the village hall.

SUNDAY SERVICE: 11.00 (3rd), 6.00 (1st, 2nd, 4th & 5th)
KEY AVAILABLE: from Mrs Harrison, Sandhall Cottage, Sandhall Lane, or from office of Alderwasley Hall School
P & wc

BALLIDON All Saints

SK 203 544

This tiny, isolated chapel in Bradbourne parish is of Norman origin. It is literally in a field and is approached by a narrow path from a stile in the roadside wall. High on the inside west wall is a fireplace which once heated a priest's overnight room. Counterweighted brass chandeliers give a stylishly dignified touch to the interior. The C15 octagonal font is curious in having many of its decorative items upside down!

SUNDAY SERVICES: temporarily suspended
CONTACT: (01335) 390570 (Mr Castledine) or (01335) 390335 (Mrs Stafford)
Publication: "The Churches of Brassington, Bradbourne & Ballidon"
P (street)

BONSALL St James

SK 280 582

Bonsall is a small hill-village on the high ground west of the Heights of Abraham. With a large church, an ancient market cross and a number of good C17 and C18 houses, it was clearly once a more important place than its present remoteness would suggest; as well as being involved in the lead mining industry general to the area it also became a flourishing centre for framework knitting. The church, of C13 origin, stands in a prominent position overlooking the village. It has a C15 tower surrounded by stone crowns and gargoyles and surmounted by a magnificent spire decorated with ornamental bands. One of the pillars in the north arcade has a curious stone figure at its base known as The Bonsall Imp - a cross between a frog and a unicorn. There is much more to see, all clearly described in the information sheets available in the church. A major restoration project was initiated in 1997.

SUNDAY SERVICE: 9.30 (1st, 3rd, 4th, 5th), 11.00 (2nd)
KEY AVAILABLE: from Mr Gregory, 35 Church Street
CONTACT: (01629) 822896 (Team Vicar)
FLOWER FESTIVAL: 3rd week June
OPEN FOR WELL DRESSING:
last w/e July
Publication: "Bonsall, a Portrait
of a Village and its Church"
(available fromScarthin
Books, Cromford)
P (street - limited)
♿ WC

St James, Bonsall

BRADBOURNE All Saints (Grade I)

SK 208 527

This church is full of interest, both inside and out. Seen from the Bradbourne Brook (to the west) the massive Norman tower on its hillside site looks like a castle keep. Close up the tower has the unusual feature of a highly ornamented C12 doorway on its south side: it may have been moved (an early conservation exercise, perhaps?) from the south wall of the nave when an aisle was built in the C13. Even older than the Norman tower is the C11 Saxon masonry of the north wall. Following the standard alterations to windows and roofs that took place during the Perpendicular period the building has remained virtually unchanged. One can only list the treasures to be found within the church: a Saxon cross, some C14/C15 glass, a C16/C17 mural, an Italian C17 oil painting of the Adoration and four carved oak panels of uncertain origin.

SUNDAY SERVICES: 11.00 (alternate weeks), 6.00
CONTACT: (01335) 390570 (Mr Castledine) or (01335) 390335 (Mrs Stafford)
Publication: "The Churches of Brassington, Bradbourne & Ballidon"
Ⓟ (in drive)

BRASSINGTON St James

SK 230 543

The limestone hill-village enjoys a magnificent south-facing slope with spectacular views. The church is on a higher level and looks down over the old houses and narrow lanes. The tower, unusually for a Norman structure, has two buttresses on the south side - no doubt on account of the steep slope of the land in that direction. Inside there is a fine Norman south nave arcade of three bays together with (unusually) a further two bays of Norman aisle and arcading on the south side of the chancel. Within the tower is a stone carving, possibly older than the tower itself, of a naked man with his hand on his heart - "the oldest inhabitant of Brassington". On the north side of the chancel is the historic 1859 Forster & Andrews organ containing pipes and casework from an even earlier instrument. At night the church is floodlit - something worth seeing from the southern approach to the village.

SUNDAY SERVICE: 9.30 (1st, 2nd, 4th), 11.00 (3rd), 6.00 (5th)
CHURCH OPEN: daily,, 10.00-6.00 (May till October)
OPEN FOR BRASSINGTON WAKES: 4th week July
CONTACT: (01629) 822896 (Team Vicar)
Publications: "St James Brassington" and "The Churches of Brassington, Bradbourne & Ballidon"   Ⓟ (street)

CARSINGTON St Margaret

SK 253 534

The small C12 chapel was completely rebuilt in the C17 - "Re-edified 1648", as the sundial on the south wall proclaims. The style is still Perpendicular - an interesting example of Gothic survival from an era not noted for its church building. The west gallery, now containing the organ, dates from 1704 and its front is heavily carved in a manner still reminiscent of Jacobean style.

SUNDAY SERVICE: 11.00
CHURCH OPEN: daily, 9.00 till dusk
CONTACT: (01629) 540392 (Mrs Brown) or (01629) 540418 (Mr & Mrs Springall)
P (street)

CROMFORD St Mary

SK 299 571

The history of St Mary's Church, of Willersley Castle, of the mill complex and, indeed, of the whole village is linked to one figure: Sir Richard Arkwright. It was his vision that recognized the potential of the site and it was his dynamic drive that caused Cromford eventually to become a shrine, revered as a cradle of the Industrial Revolution. St Mary's was commenced by Arkwright as a chapel for the Castle but was only completed in 1797, five years after his death. The building was Gothicized in 1858 by H I Stevens. Wall paintings (at present the subject of restoration plans) and most of the stained glass are by A O Hemming (1897). There are tombs and monuments to various members of the Arkwright family.

SUNDAY SERVICE: 9.30
CONTACT: (01629) 582947 (Vicar)
P (public CP)   ⚲ ♿ wc

DARLEY (or DARLEY DALE) St Helen, Church Lane

SK 266 629

A large, cruciform church, of C13 origin though with much C15 work in evidence. The oldest of its monuments is the stone tomb of the cross-legged knight, Sir John de Darley (c1330). Later graves include those of the Manchester armaments manufacturer, Sir Joseph Whitworth, and his family, great benefactors of the village. The churchyard contains a huge yew tree with possibly the largest girth in England (33 feet in circumference).

SUNDAY SERVICES: 8.00, 10.30
CONTACT: (01629) 732069 (Mrs Church) or (01629) 734257 (Rector)

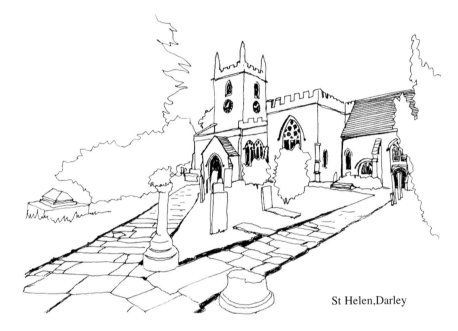

St Helen,Darley

DARLEY DALE Dale Road Methodist, Dale Road North

SK 274 629

The stylish Gothic front of this chapel next-door to the imposing Whitworth Institute is a familiar feature on the main A6 road through the Dale. Opened in 1904, it replaced an earlier Wesleyan chapel in the area to the east known as Two Dales. It possesses an interesting 3-manual Conacher organ that came from a private residence.

SUNDAY SERVICES: 10.30, 6.30
KEY AVAILABLE: from Manse (next door) : (01629) 732228 (Minister)
P wc

DETHICK St John the Baptist

SK 327 580

This must be one of the most fascinating church locations in Derbyshire. During the C13 a manor house and adjacent chapel were built by Geoffrey Dethick. The chapel was basic, with simple lancet windows (of which two survive). By the C15 the manor had come into the possession of the Babington family, and it was their most famous member, Anthony (of Mary Queen of Scots plot fame), who during 1530-32 set about improving the chapel. He raised the roof by adding a set of Perpendicular style clerestory windows - though still without any aisle and with no architectural division between nave and sanctuary - and built the superb tower which is such a notable feature of this small and otherwise still quite simple church. It remained a chapelry of Ashover until 1900 when it acquired its own parochial status (though the needs of the parish are nowadays generally served by the newer church at nearby Holloway). The immediate surroundings are still manorial, consisting of a cluster of historic farms through which one passes to reach the church. Once there the views are stunning - visitors are recommended to walk some of the footpaths across the fields to the south of the church in order to look back at the general ensemble.

SUNDAY SERVICE: 11.00 (monthly, on 1st Sun)
KEY AVAILABLE: from Manor Farm (next door) : (01629) 534275 (Mrs Groom)
Ⓟ (on main road, not in farm lane)

ELTON All Saints

SK 222 610

A simple, lancet Gothic church of 1812, alongside the main street of a small village whose C18 cottages bear witness to its former lead-mining history. Though not large, the interior of this church always seems light and bright - an open space without galleries (though there are traces of one having been at the west end). The charming little chamber organ with a classical, pedimented case was built by Bevington & Sons in the 1850's and came from a church in St Alban's.

SUNDAY SERVICE: 8.00 (1st), 11.15 (2nd), 11.00 (3rd), 6.00 (4th),(As advertised on 5th)
CHURCH OPEN: daily, 9.00-6.00
CONTACT: (01629) 650256 (Incumbent)
Ⓟ (street)

HACKNEY Methodist, Greenaway Lane

SK 285 623

Serving one of the numerous small communities spread along the general area of Darley Dale, the 1908 former Primitive Methodist chapel in Gothic style replaced a tiny early C19 one which can still be seen nearby. From the rear there is a fine view over the Dale.

SUNDAY SERVICE: 10.30
CONTACT: (01629) 732228 (Minister)
P WC

HOLLOWAY (or LEA & HOLLOWAY) Christ Church, Church Street

SK 323 570

Though strictly a chapel of ease within the parish of Dethick (see above) this church has been built where most of the parishioners actually live and it now serves the major part of their needs. It is an impressive building in free Perpendicular Gothic style by P H Currey (1903), without transepts but with a massive central tower (added in 1911). The glass in the east window (1919) is a good example of the work of Louis Davis in the Arts and Crafts style. The church occupies a prominent place on the hillside; from it the views across the scenic Lea valley need to be experienced.

SUNDAY SERVICES: 8.30 (1st & 2nd), 11.00 (2nd, 3rd, 4th & 5th), 3.00 (2nd & 4th)
CONTACT: (01629) 534275 (Vicar)
P (street) 🚪 ♟ ♿ WC

HOLLOWAY Trinity Methodist, Church Street

SK 324 566

This attractive stone chapel is in lancet-Gothic style and occupies a dramatic hillside site. It originated in 1852 as one of six Wesleyan Reform chapels built by John Smedley, the local textile manufacturer, whose mill still functions in the valley below. Smedley's characteristic liturgical aspirations resulted in "churchy" structures with towers, bells and chancels - not to mention a specially devised prayer book! In 1879 the building was enlarged sideways and re-orientated internally through 90 degrees, so removing the pseudo-

Anglican effect from the interior; the former "chancel" was partitioned off as a schoolroom.

SUNDAY SERVICES: 10.45 (weekly) & 6.30 (monthly, as advertised)
CHURCH OPEN: Fri 10.00-12.00 ("coffee & chat") & often at other times
KEY AVAILABLE: from house opposite; visitors may also be shown round by Mr John Daglish (01629) 534479
P (in street, but, please, not directly outside) **wc**

IDRIDGEHAY St James

SK 286 490

This small church, only 50 feet long, on a cramped, triangular site, represents H I Stevens at his most ingenious. It was built in 1855 in C14 Gothic style and has all the features of a much larger building - nave, chancel and wide north aisle, all with high, steeply pitched roofs. The tower is to the north of the chancel, its ground floor forming the vestry; the broached spire reaches up to 94 feet. With floor space at a premium the small Bevington organ (1876) is against the north chancel wall, its bellows and pipework all cantilevered out over the single keyboard. In the churchyard is the grave of George Turner, the local artist sometimes referred to as "Derbyshire's Constable".

SUNDAY SERVICE: 11.00
CONTACT: (01773) 550138 (Mrs Hopkinson) or (01773) 550625 (Mrs White)
Publication: F Long, "St James's, Idridgehay Church History"
P (street)

MATLOCK Methodist & United Reformed, Bank Road/Oak Road

SK 301 604

The former Wesleyan chapel is a substantial building in the Arts & Crafts Gothic style of 1904, with a fine tower and spire, prominently positioned half way up the steep Bank Road. As built the chancel had a distinctly Edwardian Anglican feel in its arrangement of holy table, choirstalls, pulpit and organ chamber. Refurbishment in 1997, however, has changed much of this: the interior is now modernized and re-arranged, with comfortable seating and full disabled facilities (including a lift).

SUNDAY SERVICES: 10.30, 6.30
CHURCH OPEN: Fri 12.00-1.30 (for lunch) & by arrangement
CHURCH OFFICE: (01629) 55809
Ⓟ 🛆 ⊠ (Fri) ♿ [wc]

MATLOCK BANK All Saints, Smedley Street

SK 298 608

This might indeed have been a wonderful church had it ever been completed. What we have is a large, lofty choir completed in 1884 to a design by T H and F Healey, together with a part of a nave hastily finished in truncated form at a later date. In the east wall there are three lancets with a rose above, all with glass by William Morris to Burne-Jones designs. The organ is a grand instrument by Forster & Andrews (1886), well suited to the building.

SUNDAY SERVICES: 8.00, 10.30, 6.30
CHURCH OPEN: daily, 9.00-12.00
KEY AVAILABLE: from Mr Turner, 163 Smedley Street : (01629) 583906
Ⓟ ♿

MATLOCK BATH Holy Trinity

SK 295 579

The spa village of Matlock Bath stretches along a strip of the west bank of the Derwent at a point where the valley is both narrow and steeply sided, giving it something of the character of the small towns in the Mosel Valley and its tributaries. The church, with its slender spire, dates from 1842 and is prettily situated alongside the A6 road. The chancel was extended (with a new reredos) in 1874. Much interior re-ordering and refurbishing has taken place in recent decades - a particularly unusual feature being the new Baptistry designed for adult immersion.

SUNDAY SERVICE: 10.45
CHURCH OFFICE: (01629) 583924 (Office)
Ⓟ 🛆 ⚲ [wc]

Holy Trinity, Middleton-by-Wirksworth

MIDDLETON-BY-WIRKSWORTH Congregational

SK 278 560

The chapel and graveyard, in a listed conservation area, occupy an elevated site, 1,000 feet above sea level, at the top end of the steeply rising, former lead mining village; the view over the rest of Middleton and down to Wirksworth itself is very impressive. It was first built in 1786 and from this period survive the "Gothick" arch to the choir recess and the flat ceiling. Externally, however, the chapel was refashioned in the late C19 and a schoolroom was added. The prized possession is a hexagonal pulpit of c1695 from the hymn writer Philip Doddridge's Castle Hill Meeting House in Northampton. The chapel also has a fine Lloyd organ of c1880.

SUNDAY SERVICE: 2.30
CONTACT: (01629) 823542 (Don Hamilton)

MIDDLETON-BY-WIRKSWORTH Holy Trinity

SK 279 556

The church, on a steeply sloping site, dates from 1838 and is a simple, chapel-like structure in Perpendicular Gothic style - a single room with west gallery, an altar against the east wall and an organ in the NE corner. Like many a hillside chapel it makes good use of the terrain by having schoolrooms underneath. The organ is an excellent 2-manual instrument by Lloyd (c1885) - mothballed at present pending its hoped-for restoration when funds allow.

SUNDAY SERVICE: 11.00 (1st, 3rd, 4th, 5th), 6.00 (2nd)
KEY AVAILABLE: from Burrows Farm Bungalow, New Road
CONTACT: (01629) 822896 (Team Vicar)
P (street) ♿

SOUTH DARLEY (or WENSLEY) St Mary the Virgin
SK 267 616

The church serves the communities of Darley Bridge and Wensley, on the road leading up from Darley Dale to the old lead-mining village of Winster. It dates from the 1840's and is in an attractive neo-Norman style with a chancel added in 1866. It has an east window by Morris & Co.

SUNDAY SERVICE: 9.00 (1st & 3rd), 6.30 (2nd), (4th & 5th as advertised)
CHURCH OPEN: daily, 9.00-6.00
CONTACT: (01629) 650256 (Incumbent)
P (street)

TANSLEY Holy Trinity, Church Street
SK 323 599

As built in 1840 the church was a simple box with plain lancet windows, a shallow sanctuary recess and a small tower - much as it still looks when approached from the south. In 1870, however, a new north aisle was built in a more academic Gothic style and the box pews were replaced. One of the lancet windows in the south aisle contains a fine stained glass depiction of the Archangel Uriel by Ford Madox Brown, probably of the 1860's and acquired in 1941. The bowl of the font came from the village church of Derwent, now submerged under Ladybower Reservoir. The organ, in the west gallery, contains some ranks of pipes from an early C19 barrel instrument originally in Lincolnshire.

SUNDAY SERVICES: 9.30, 6.00
CHURCH OPEN: daily
Publication: D Gaskell, "Holy Trinity Church Tansley 1840-1990"
CONTACT: (01629) 534275 (Incumbent)
P (street) □ ♀ ♂ ♿ wc

TANSLEY Methodist, Church Street

SK 323 596

The small Wesleyan chapel bears the inscription: "open'd December 25th 1829"; but the tablet has been reset suggesting a rebuild or enlargement at a later date. The chapel is set back from the street and in front is what is referred to as the "Dissenters' Graveyard".

SUNDAY SERVICES: 10.30, 6.00
KEY AVAILABLE: Caretaker lives on site
P (street) wc

WENSLEY Methodist, Main Road

SK 265 613

Like the one at Tansley this is a small Wesleyan chapel built in 1829 and enlarged in 1879. Behind the pulpit is a fine, exposed stone wall. The chapel is noted as being the birthplace of the Methodist Local Preachers' Mutual Aid Association.

SUNDAY SERVICE: 6.15 (3.00 in winter)
CONTACT: (01629) 734894 (Mrs Taylor) or (01629) 732228 (Minister)
P (difficult!)

WINSTER Methodist, East Bank

SK 241 605

Built in 1823 (and enlarged in 1850) this is the fifth oldest Primitive Methodist chapel in the whole country. It has pews arranged in tiers. Access, however, is difficult - by footpath only from East Bank. The village (population 693) also boasts two other Methodist chapels - a Wesleyan (now a residence) and a tiny, independent Wesleyan Reform (still in use).

SUNDAY SERVICE: 2.30
CONTACT: (01629) 650582 (Mr Marshall) or (01629) 732228 (Minister)
P (lower down East Bank) wc

St Mary, Wirksworth

WINSTER St John the Baptist

SK 239 606

A delightfully whimsical church of considerable architectural interest. The oldest part is the tower of 1721 in plain Georgian style with only a clock as decoration. Adjoining this is the nave, rebuilt by M Habershon in 1842 with tall, two-light Gothic windows. The most remarkable alteration came next, in 1883, when the church was widened northwards by creating two identical naves divided by an arcade of slim, elegant arches. These converge by means of diagonal arches at the east end to lead into the chancel - a truly unique architectural composition. A small, south window in the chancel, by the organ, is by Burne-Jones (1887). Local legend has it that the last public duel in England was fought in Winster churchyard.

SUNDAY SERVICE: 10.00
CHURCH OPEN: daily, 9.00-6.00
OPEN FOR WAKES WEEK: from Sun following 24 June
CONTACT: (01629) 650256 (Vicar)   🅿 (street)

WIRKSWORTH Baptist, Coldwell Street

SK 288 540

Built of gritstone in 1886 and now within the Wirksworth Conservation Area, this is a well preserved example of a larger Victorian Gothic Baptist church. Steps lead up to the front porch (chair lift available from side door) leading to an interior whose sloping floor gives all seats a good view of pulpit and baptistry. Below the main church are schoolroom, classrooms and kitchen.

SUNDAY SERVICE: 10.45 + occasional 6.00 united (in rotating locations)
CHURCH OPEN: Tue 10.00-12.00 ("Coffee for Shoppers" - Market Day)
CHURCH OFFICE: (01629) 825971
P (Market Place or Barmote) 🛉 💺 ♿ wc

WIRKSWORTH St Mary

SK 287 539

Why this outstanding church is not listed Grade "A" or "I" is difficult to understand - it can only be due to the amount of "restoration" that took place at three different stages in the C19. St Mary's is a large, cruciform building standing within a cathedral-like close of old houses which surround the large churchyard. Much of it dates from C13, C14 and C15 though there are earlier fragments. For such a large church the nave, though wide, is unusually short - of only three bays. Beyond the central tower the chancel and sanctuary together are considerably longer. The transepts are also long, both having eastern aisles, and there are sizeable chapels north and south of the chancel. A Saxon stone coffin lid of c800, now in the north wall, shows scenes from the life of Christ. Another Romanesque carving shows a king and queen. Among the various monuments those of Anthony Lowe (1555) and local benefactor, Anthony Gell (1583), are particularly noteworthy. Of interest in the churchyard is the tomb of Matthew Pear, aged 109.

SUNDAY SERVICES: 8.00 (1st), 9.30, 6.00
CHURCH OPEN: daily, 9.00 till dusk
"CLYPPING SERVICE": Sun on or after 8 September (part of historic Wirksworth Festival, traditionally associated with dedication feast of St Mary's Parish Church)
WELL DRESSING: May Bank Holiday Weekend
P (street or public CP) 🛉 ♿

MELBOURNE

BARROW-ON-TRENT St Wilfrid, Church Lane (Grade I)

SK 354 284

Barrow is a small village on the north bank of the Trent. The church has a C13 north nave arcade though most of the rest is of the following century. The chancel walls protrude some distance into the nave, with squints provided each side to allow for viewing of the altar from the east ends of the aisles. There is a C14 alabaster effigy of a priest.

SUNDAY SERVICE: 10.00
KEY AVAILABLE: from Mr Woolley, 18 Hall Park
P (on nearby turf)

CALKE St Giles, Calke Abbey

SK 369 224

The church is delightfully situated in the landscaped park about half a mile from the house itself. It was built in 1826 and contains tombs of the Harpur family from an earlier chapel on the site. In the west gallery is a 3-stop barrel organ by H C Lincoln (c1840). The church is now administered by the National Trust.

CHURCH OPEN: at Calke Abbey opening times, as advertised by National Trust

MELBOURNE Baptist, Chapel Street

SK 386 254

Though visible from High Street through a large and mature graveyard, the main frontage of this listed building is in Chapel Street, to the east. The first chapel was built in 1750 and some original masonry may still be seen in a side wall. A major rebuilding and enlargement, with galleries, took place in 1832 with an extension in 1856 for the organ loft. The interior front end now presents a fine late 19th century ensemble; the preacher's view from the pulpit, however, is still very much that of 1832. Thomas ("Thos.") Cook,

founder of the travel agency and a native of Melbourne, was a licensed
Evangelist and Sunday School Superintendent here in the 1820's.

SUNDAY SERVICES: 10.30, 6.00
CONTACT: (01332) 865215 (Minister) or (01332) 863252 (Mrs Hewlett)
ANNUAL FLOWER FESTIVAL: June
Publication: T J Budge, "Melbourne Baptists"
P (in Chapel St) & wc

St Michael & St Mary, Melbourne

MELBOURNE St Michael & St Mary (Grade I)

SK 389 250

Save for its lamentably rebuilt and reduced chancel this is a large, complete
and very lavish Norman cruciform building, dating from the mid-12th century
and in a remarkable state of preservation. This, coupled with its setting amidst
a "cathedral close"-like assortment of old buildings and its proximity to

Melbourne Hall and Lake, makes it one of the most frequently visited churches in the county. Awareness of this important visitor responsibility is reflected (most creditably) in the well-stocked stall containing guide-books in various foreign languages.

SUNDAY SERVICES: 8.00, 10.00, 6.30
CHURCH OPEN: daily, 9.30-5.00 (earlier in winter)
Publication: F Ross, "Melbourne Parish Church"
(in full colour and available in several languages)
Ⓟ 🏛 🅟 ♟ 🚶 (Sun only) 🖂 (Sun only) ♿ 🚻 (Sun only)

SMISBY St James (Grade I)

SK 348 191

The small village shows many signs of its mediaeval past. The earliest part of the church is the south aisle - the original Norman chapel of ease. Nave and chancel were added in the early C14 by Joan Comyn (of Smisby Manor): her alabaster effigy (1350) lies next to the C14 font. Some C16 linenfold panelling at the east end is from nearby Ashby-de-la-Zouch Castle (Leicestershire). Sir Walter Scott wrote "Ivanhoe" after ascending the church tower and seeing the old tournament field in the valley between Smisby and Ashby.

SUNDAY SERVICE: 5.30
CONTACT: (01283) 217319 (Mr & Mrs Barnes)
Publication: "St James Church Smisby"
Ⓟ (street)

STANTON-BY-BRIDGE St Michael (Grade I)

SK 367 271

The Bridge in question, of course, is the half mile long mediaeval Swarkeston Bridge over the Trent - a magnificently hazardous obstacle course for traffic! The church contains both Saxon and Norman masonry in the nave. The rest is later C13. Interesting monuments include a recess with an effigy of a priest (c1400) and an alabaster slab to William Sacheverell (1558).

SUNDAY SERVICES: no information
CONTACT: (01332) 864707 (Mr Jenkins)
Ⓟ (street)

TICKNALL Methodist, Chapel Street

SK 354 241

Deep red brick former Wesleyan chapel, built in 1815, with Flemish shaped gable at the front and a double row of square sash windows all round. As a listed building it is an important element in a most attractive early C19 estate village created by the Harpur-Crewes of nearby Calke Abbey (NT), now a conservation area. Even more exciting is the interior - a delightfully preserved late Georgian ensemble with original galleries on three sides, rostrum and pulpit. Only the downstairs pews have been renewed. The chamber organ, with its "Gothick" case, dates from 1841 and was acquired from "another chapel".

SUNDAY SERVICE: 6.00 (3.00 in winter)
CONTACT: (01332) 863958 (Mr Adams)
P (public CP at village hall) wc

TICKNALL St George

SK 351 241

Ticknall is an attractive estate village, now a conservation area, linked to nearby Calke Abbey. Fragments of the original church still remain in the churchyard south of the present building - the latter being to a large and well proportioned Perpendicular Gothic design by H I Stevens (1842). Inside, from the old church, are the recessed effigy of a civilian and an incised slab to a knight, both of the C14. The historic organ was installed by J W Walker in 1869.

SUNDAY SERVICE: 9.30
CONTACT: (01332) 862647 (Mrs Hirst)
P (street)

 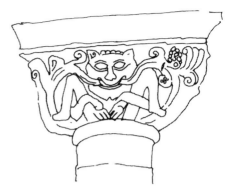

The Melbourne Cat. St Michael with St Mary, Melbourne

Sheela na gig. St Michael with St Mary, Melbourne

TWYFORD St Andrew (Grade I)

SK 328 287

Until 1963 the village street led to a chain ferry over the Trent, but is now a cul-de-sac. The village itself, with a population of little over 100, is merely a cluster of houses by the river bank. The church has much to offer: Norman chevroned chancel arch, C13 tower, C14 chancel, C15 spire and - if that were not enough - a nave that was refashioned in the C18 with red brick outer facing walls and round-headed windows. Monuments inside reflect local families - the Harpurs (of Calke) and Vernons (of Sudbury). The small organ, with a mid C19 case reflecting the Norman chancel arch, is said to contain some pipes of a 1790 instrument.

SUNDAY SERVICE: 11.00 or 4.00 (alternately)
CHURCH OPEN: daily (otherwise key from The Grange, next door)
Publication: "The Church of Saint Andrew Twyford"
P (Church Lane or Riverside) ♿ WC (in The Grange)

REPTON & SWADLINCOTE

CALDWELL St Giles, Church Lane

SK 253 172

An ancient chapelry, adjacent to Caldwell Hall and still displaying signs of its Norman origin despite Victorian refurbishment. Contents of interest include some stained glass roundels of c1400 and the early C19 chamber organ (installed in 1996).

SUNDAY SERVICE: 10.00
KEY AVAILABLE: from Mrs Mizuro, Church Farm, Church Lane
P

COTON-IN-THE-ELMS St Mary, Church Street

SK 244 154

The village is square in plan and was once lined with elms - which unfortunately succombed to the Dutch Elm Disease of the 1960's. The church is by H I Stevens, 1846, with tower and spire and a plain, wide nave without aisles. Plans are under way to refurbish the interior.

SUNDAY SERVICE: 11.30 (3rd), 6.30 (1st, 2nd, 4th & 5th)
CONTACT: (01283) 760811 (Mrs Scott)
P (street)   Other facilities planned

FINDERN All Saints, The Green

SK 309 305

All Saints is most attractively situated overlooking the village green. Designed by Stevens & Robinson it dates from 1864, though a Norman tympanum reminds us of the previous building, together with an incised slab to Isbella de Fynderne, 1444.

SUNDAY SERVICE: 9.30
CONTACT: (01283) 701307 (Mr Chisnall)
P   🛈   ⚲

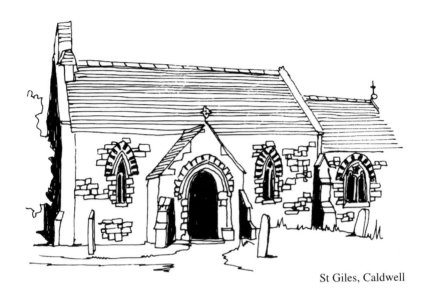

St Giles, Caldwell

FOREMARK St Saviour (Grade I)

SK 329 226

From the Milton-Ingleby road take the HGV track to Foremark Hall (Repton Preparatory School); park on grass triangle in front of church. It may be slightly difficult to find but it is certainly worth the effort. The church is important on two accounts - for its architecture and for its furnishings. Built in 1662 it is not only one of the few Restoration churches outside London, but it is still in a surviving form of Perpendicular Gothic - battlemented tower and nave with depressed arch windows. Once inside we discover a totally unrestored "Prayer Book" interior, with contemporary box pews, communicants' pews, screen, chancel panelling, communion table, font and 3-decker pulpit. In addition to all this the wrought iron communion rails are by Robert Bakewell (c1710) - as are also the churchyard gates leading towards the Hall.

SUNDAY SERVICE: 8.00 (4th only), 6.30 (2nd only)
CHURCH OPEN: daily ℗

HARTSHORNE St Peter, Church Street

SK 327 208

Tower and chancel are of the C15 but the nave was rebuilt in 1835. The window traceries of the latter are of cast iron as are the columns supporting

St. Wystan, Repton

the west gallery (and organ). There is an interesting alabaster monument (1599) to Humphrey Dethick, his wife and family.

SUNDAY SERVICES: 8.30 (1st & 3rd), 10.30 (weekly)
CONTACT: (01283) 217866 (Rector)
P (lane at side)   🕭   ⚲   ♿   wc

REPTON St Wystan (Grade I)

SK 303 272

At first glance this is a fairly typical, large Gothic church, mainly of the 14th century, with an unusually tall spire reaching up to 212 feet - a church that many a village or town would be proud to possess. But enshrined within is something even more special, for on a site where the first Christians came to Mercia in 654 we have the substantial remnant of a 9th century Saxon minster built over an 8th century crypt. The latter, originally a burial chamber for the South Mercian King, Wiglaf, became the shrine of his canonized grandson, Wystan, murdered in 849. The crypt remains intact and may be entered by the little stairs in the SE corner of the north nave aisle, while the upper church is still visible in the walls of the chancel and in some of the masonry at the eastern end of the nave. On a site to the east of the church is the oldest part of Repton School, founded in the 16th century and using the buildings of the dissolved Augustinian Priory. In the south east chapel now stands the fine modern organ by Peter Collins (1998) with its spectacular casework inspired by that of Old Radnor (C16 - the earliest in Britain).

SUNDAY SERVICES: 8.00, 10.00, 6.30
CHURCH OPEN: daily, 8.15 till 8.00 (or till dusk in winter)
Publications: H M Taylor, "St. Wystan's Church Repton" There is also an interesting brochure, "Repton Trail", by Repton Village History Group
P   🕭   ⚲   ♿

ROSLISTON St Mary

SK 244 169

The C14 tower with its rebuilt broach spire still remains. The nave, however, is of 1819 - a wide, aisleless structure with three large, two-light Gothic windows in each of its side walls, the middle one on the south wall having its lower half replaced by a porch. The shallow sanctuary, only slightly less wide than the nave, has the uniquely attractive feature of a triple chancel arch - a transverse arcade in which the central arch is just marginally larger than the two side ones. Save for the later Victorian furnishings the interior is quite unaltered and well worth a visit.

SUNDAY SERVICE: 8.45 (2nd to 5th), 10.30 (1st only)
CONTACT: (01283) 761416 (Mrs Leedham) or (01283) 761436 (Mrs Marbrow)
Ⓟ (street)

SWADLINCOTE Emmanuel, Church Street
SK 303196

Designed by H I Stevens this church has altered little from its completion in 1846: no tower, aisleless nave, transepts and apsidal sanctuary. Bomb damage in the First World War almost precipitated a total rebuilding, but the plans were eventually modified to take the form of a refurbishment of the existing church - the only exterior alteration being the removal of a bellcote from the west gable.

SUNDAY SERVICES: 10.00, 6.30
CONTACT: (01283) 217756 (Vicar)
Publications: C Jackson, "Emmanuel the Parish Church of Swadlincote"
C Jackson, "Notes for a Walk round Swadlincote Parish Church"
Ⓟ ◻ ⚲ ♿ �︼WC

WALTON-UPON-TRENT St Laurence, Station Lane
SK 216 183

Walton is linked to Staffordshire, over the river, by a temporary Bailey bridge, from where there is a pleasant view of the village. The church is large, with plenty that is of interest, in particular the substantial Perpendicular tower and the late Norman south arcade; the chancel is C13 with trefoiled sedilia, while the large south transept was a chantry, founded in 1334. Amongst later items of interest are a small, but very effective Bevington organ of c1870 and some fine early C20 wood carving in the choirstalls and elsewhere by a Rector of the period.

SUNDAY SERVICE: 8.45 (1st), 10.00 (2nd to 5th)
CONTACT: (01283) 712072 (Mr Hanslow) or (01283) 713506 (Mr Adams, History Consultant) Ⓟ (street)

WILLINGTON St Michael, Hall Lane

SK 295 283

A small, plain nave and chancel, possibly of Norman origin, without aisles but with a very large north transept of c1824. Of this same date is the flat plaster ceiling throughout. Leaning against the chancel wall is an incised slab memorial to a C17 organist (where? - not here, surely!). The attractiveness of the interior - albeit somewhat lopsided in shape - is in its simple, pre-Victorian elegance. Well worth a visit.

SUNDAY SERVICE: 11.00 (1st & 3rd), 6.00 (2nd, 4th & 5th)
KEY USUALLY AVAILABLE: details in porch
Publication: "The Church of St Michael Willington"
🅿 ♿

SOME SUGGESTED THEMATIC TRAILS

Not all of the churches or chapels included in these "trails" have supplied information about opening times for inclusion in this book. Prospective visitors should therefore check the details in the text - some places that are not included may quite well turn out to be open; in other instances a view of the exterior will have to suffice.

BAGSHAWE TRAIL (northern area)

William Bagshawe was baptized at TIDESWELL in 1628 and ordained in 1650 at CHESTERFIELD into the Presbyterian form of ministry current during the Commonwealth period. Following the restoration of the monarchy and the subsequent Act of Uniformity, he was (like many others) ejected in 1662 from his living as Vicar of GLOSSOP and became an itinerant preacher, earning for himself the nickname of "The Apostle of the Peak". During this period of his ministry he founded independent Presbyterian congregations at BRADWELL (latterly Unitarian - the chapel now closed and used for other purposes), CHINLEY (now Independent Congregational) and GREAT HUCKLOW (now Unitarian); he is also known to have preached at CHARLESWORTH (now Independent Congregational). He died in 1702 at the family home of FORD HALL and was buried in the chancel of the local parish church at CHAPEL-EN-LE-FRITH (which he had regularly attended in order to pay lip-service to the law requiring attendance at parish worship on the Lord's Day!).

BAKEWELL TRAIL (central and southern areas)

Robert Bakewell, 1682-1752, the celebrated craftsman in iron, was born at Uttoxeter (just in Staffordshire). He established himself in London, filling a niche in the market conveniently vacated by the great Jean Tijou. His popularity in and around Derby seems to have resulted from a commission by Thomas Coke of Melbourne Hall. The finest collection of Bakewell ironwork is to be seen in DERBY CATHEDRAL, with its great gated screen and numerous other fittings. Disregarding (for our purposes) his important work in private houses, other examples of his ecclesiastical craftsmanship are at ALVASTON (former reredos & table), ASHBOURNE (churchyard gates), BORROWASH (chancel screen), DUFFIELD (weather vane), ETWALL (almshouse gates leading into churchyard), FOREMARK (communion rails & churchyard gates) and RADBOURNE (weather vane). It is also worth a visit just over the border into Leicestershire to view the splendid screen in the NT church at Staunton Harold.

CATHOLIC CHAPELS TRAIL (northern area)

"Under-cover" (or "recusant") Roman Catholics survived in considerable strength in the Dales during the repressions of the post-Reformation centuries. Prior to the official re-establishment of a parochial system in the mid 19th century, a number of "chapels" were built at the expense of wealthy Catholic patrons such as the Eyre family at Hassop Hall. Some of these chapels (like the original one in Derby, built by the Earl of Shrewsbury) were later replaced by substantial parish churches; the survivors comprise HATHERSAGE (c1690), HASSOP (1816-18) and the slightly later example at GLOSSOP (All Saints : 1836) - all in Classical style. The mediaeval chapel at PADLEY is exceptional: Padley Hall itself had been the home of the Catholic branch of the Fitzherberts and had maintained its worship during the troubled centuries. Following abandonment and partial ruination of the building the remnants were acquired by the Catholic community and the chapel repaired and re-consecrated in 1933.

DERWENT "MILL CHURCHES" TRAIL (central area)

The Derwent Valley is currently proposed as a World Heritage Site. During the C18 and early C19 numerous mills, with their supporting communities, sprang up along the length of the river from Derby northwards. Almost invariably the mill owners furnished these villages with churches and other social facilities. To list them in geographical progression we have: DARLEY ABBEY St Matthew (Evans: 1819), BELPER Unitarian (Strutt: 1788), ALDERWASLEY All Saints (Hurt: 1850), HOLLOWAY Methodist (Smedley: 1852) and CROMFORD St Mary (Arkwright: 1797).

"ESTATE CHURCHES" TRAIL (southern area)

The south of the County has several country houses (great and small) with their associated estates. The mediaeval pattern was for the lord or squire to build the parish church where it suited his own convenience - ie next to his residence. Examples of this may be found at CALKE, ELVASTON, FOREMARK, KEDLESTON, LONGFORD, RADBOURNE and SUDBURY. A later development, in the C19, was for a "model" estate village to be built with its own church, such as may be found at BRETBY and TICKNALL (part of the Calke Estate).

HUNSTONE TRAIL (northern area)

"Old" Advent Hunstone was the most celebrated member of a family firm of wood carvers based in Tideswell. Advent himself flourished in the late C19 and early C20. His work was firmly rooted in a good understanding of late (ie Perpendicular) Gothic style, but within this parameter he was able to produce a profusion of natural, representational and symbolical subject matter. Nowhere can this better be seen than in his native parish church of TIDESWELL - most spectacularly in the organ case (1895) and Lady Chapel screen to which it is linked. The work here is fully described in Martin Hulbert's publication, "The Woodcarvings at Tideswell". Other churches containing Hunstone's work include: BURBAGE (lych gate), DRONFIELD (reredos

& high altar), MATLOCK St Giles (organ cases & choirstalls), MILLERS DALE (various furnishings) and WORMHILL (chancel furnishings).

STEVENS TRAIL (central & southern areas)

Henry Isaac Stevens (1806-1873), was Derby's most noted architect of the C19. Working in the early decades of Victoria's reign, he was clearly inspired by Pugin and Scott, and never lapsed into the "Georgian" Gothic of so many of the "Commissioners'" churches. His best work is probably at REPTON School Chapel (1857), where money was clearly not a problem, while at DERBY St Michael (1858 - now offices) the originality of the segmental window arches looks forward to Art Nouveau Gothic of the C20. Where there were financial restraints then he would use a simple, though still stylish, lancet Gothic formula. Much of his work consisted of so-called "restorations", which (typically of the time) often involved considerable rebuilding and alteration. Completely new designs by Stevens are to be found in the churches at ALVASTON (1856), BELPER Christ Church (1849), CLAY CROSS (1851), COTON IN THE ELMS (1846), HAZELWOOD (1840), HEATH (1853), IDRIDGEHAY (1845), OSMASTON (1845), SHARDLOW (1838 - an early work, still reminiscent of Commissioners' style), SWADLINCOTE (1848), TICKNALL (1842) and WOODVILLE (1846 - a pleasant essay in Norman style).

WESLEY TRAIL (central & northern areas)

John Wesley (1703-1791), indefatigable traveller and preacher, visited Derbyshire on a number of occasions. During the 1760's he is known to have preached in the new chapels at DERBY (St Michael's Lane, now demolished) and CRICH (still in use); then, in the 1780's, at BELPER, FAIRFIELD and HAYFIELD (in the parish church). There is also an interesting connection with Bagshawe's CHINLEY Chapel, where there is to be seen the C18 grave of former chapel minister, Revd John Bennet, and his wife, Grace, whom, in her earlier days, John Wesley had courted and wished to marry (until other counsels apparently prevailed).

FURTHER READING

Entries in the main text give titles of publications relating to individual churches or chapels. Visits may be enhanced by reading the following books of a more general nature, all containing Derbyshire refences:

D A Barton, "Discovering Chapels and Meeting Houses". Shire Publications Ltd.
G Barrass, "Methodism in Belper". Privately published
M Binney & P Burman, "Chapels & Churches: Who Cares". British Tourist Authority / Country Life
M Chatfield, "Churches the Victorians Forgot". Moorland Publishing
J S Curl, "Victorian Churches". Batsford / English Heritage
J O Drackley, "Notes on the Churches of Derbyshire". Privately published
G & J Hague & H J McLachlan, "The Unitarian Heritage". P B Godfrey
P Howell & I Sutton, "The Faber Guide to Victorian Churches". Faber & Faber / Victorian Society
M Hulbert, P Key, A Crookes & K Ellis, "A Drive Round Derwent and Wye Valley Churches". Hathersage Church publications
M Hulbert, P Key, A Crookes & K Ellis, "Off the Beaten Track" (village churches of White Peak and Dark Peak). Tideswell Church publications
R Innes-Smith, "Notable Churches of Derbyshire". Derbyshire Countryside Ltd
S Jenkins, "England's Thousand Best Churches". Allen Lane / Penguin Books
N Pevsner, "The Buildings of England - Derbyshire". Penguin Books
M Salter, "The Old Parish Churches of Derbyshire". Folly Publications
R Tomkins, "Pipe Organs in Churches & Chapels of the Derbyshire Derwent & Ecclesbourne Valleys". Scarthin Books

Royal Commission on the Historical Monuments of England, "Nonconformist Chapels and Meeting-houses - Derbyshire". HMSO

St Mary, Tissington

Index of Places